SILVER·BURDETT

Making Music

# Keyboard Accompaniments

## Teacher's Edition Part Two
## Grade 2

PEARSON

Scott
Foresman

**Editorial Offices:** Glenview, Illinois • Parsippany, New Jersey • New York, New York
**Sales Offices:** Needham, Massachusetts • Duluth, Georgia • Glenview, Illinois
Coppell, Texas • Sacramento, California • Mesa, Arizona

ISBN: 0-328-07772-0

Copyright © 2005, Pearson Education, Inc.

5 6 7 8 9 10 V039 13 12 11 10 09 08 07 06 05

# Contents

# To the Teacher

Keyboard accompaniments are provided for those songs for which the keyboard is an appropriate instrument or a reasonable substitute for authentic instruments.

The purpose of this book is to provide accompaniments for all levels of playing abilities. The chord symbols have been reproduced from the Teacher and/or Student edition and can be used by keyboard players looking for the most basic accompaniment, or for chording with instruments such as Autoharp and guitar. Harmonies in an accompaniment may differ from those on the recording and from the indicated chord symbols.

For a more elaborate treatment of instrumentation and harmonization, refer to the corresponding song recordings in the MAKING MUSIC CD package. While all of the keyboard accompaniments are in the same key as the recorded versions of the songs, occasional modulations may occur in the recordings.

The triangle-shaped indicators within an accompaniment designate the beginnings of lines of music on the student page.

# Gonna Have a Good Time

*Words and Music by Bill Schontz*
*Arranged by Joyce Kalbach*

Come on,    let's    go,    one,    two    three;    You're the on - ly one,    so dance___
Come on,    let's    go,    sev'n,    eight,    nine;    When you dance with me,    I feel___

___    with    me;    Come on,    let's    go,    four    five    six;
___    so    fine;    Come on,    let's    go,    ten,    'leven,    twelve;

D.C. al Fine

If    you    don't    dance,    I'm    in    a    fix._____
If    you    don't    dance,    I'll    dance    my - self._____

## *Heigh-Ho*  *from* Snow White and the Seven Dwarfs

Words by Larry Morey

Music by Frank Churchill
Arranged by John Richardson

"Heigh - ho,    heigh - ho,"    To    make    your trou - bles    go,
ho,    heigh - ho,"    It's    home    from work we    go,

just keep on sing-ing all day long, "Heigh - ho, heigh - ho, heigh-ho, Heigh -
(whistle or hum)_____ "Heigh - ho, heigh - ho, heigh-ho, heigh -

ho, heigh - ho, heigh - ho," For if you're feel - ing low, You
ho, heigh - ho, heigh - ho," All sev - en in a row, You (whistle

pos - i - tive-ly can't go wrong With a "heigh, heigh-ho, heigh-ho, heigh -
or hum)_____ With a "heigh, heigh- ho."

## Time to Sing

Words and Music by Raffi, D. Pike, and B. & B. Simpson
Arranged by Don Kalbach

Brightly

VERSE

1. It's time to sing a song or two. You with me and

6

2. It's time for us to clap our hands in rhythm with the beat.
   Time for hands to clap awhile,
   Hey, hey, hey. *Refrain*

3. It's time for us to tap our toes together with our feet.
   Time for toes to tap awhile,
   Hey, hey, hey. *Refrain*

4. It's time to make a sound you like.
   la la la la la la la
   la la la la la la la
   la la la *Refrain, then repeat verse 1 to Coda*

# Go Around the Corn, Sally

African American Work Song
Arranged by Carol Jay

Energetically

Solo
Go a - round, round and round, Go a - round the corn, Sal - ly.

2 Solo
Hey now, Hey now, Go a - round the corn, Sal - ly.

3 Solo
Fast - er still, Fast - er still, Round and round the corn, Sal - ly.

4 Solo
All a - round, all a - round, Go a - round the corn, Sal - ly.

## *Xiao yin chuan* (Silver Moon Boat)

*Folk Song from China*
*Arranged by Mary Jean Nelson*

**Delicately**

Yue er wan wan xiang yi tiao chuan gua tian shang, Chuan guo xing xing
Lit - tle sil - ver moon rides the sky like a boat, Past the twink - ling

ta yi ran qing ying piao dang Yang fan___ xiang zhe
stars it will float, light - ly float. Sail, lit - tle moon boat,

xi fang hang Jia xiao xiao yin chuan duo an xiang.
to the west, Sail, lit - tle moon boat, while I rest.

9

# Un pajarito (A Little Bird)

English Words by Alice Firgau

Folk Song from Spain
Arranged by Joyce Kalbach

# Michael, Row the Boat Ashore

*African American Spiritual*
*Arranged by John Girt*

1. Mi - chael, row the boat a - shore, Hal - le - lu - jah! Mi - chael,
2. Sis - ter, help to trim the sail, Hal - le - lu - jah! Sis - ter,

row the boat a - shore, Hal - le - lu - jah.
help to trim the sail, Hal - le - lu - jah.

3. River Jordan's deep and wide, . . .
   Milk and honey on the other side. . . .

4. Trumpet sound the jubilee, . . .
   Cross this river and we'll be free. . . .

11

# Lone Star Trail

*Cowboy Song from the United States*
*Arranged by Darrell Peter*

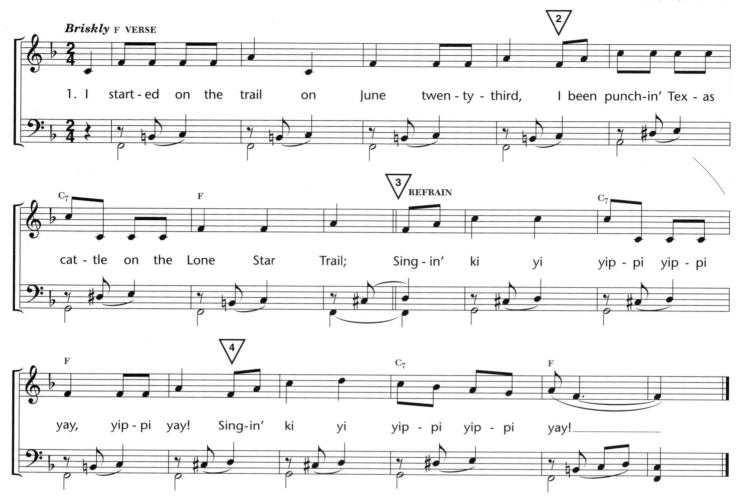

1. I start-ed on the trail on June twen-ty-third, I been punch-in' Tex-as cat-tle on the Lone Star Trail; Sing-in' ki yi yip-pi yip-pi yay, yip-pi yay! Sing-in' ki yi yip-pi yip-pi yay!

2. I'm up in the mornin' before daylight,
   And before I sleep the moon shines bright. *Refrain*

3. Oh, it's bacon and beans 'most every day,
   I'd as soon be a-eatin' prairie hay. *Refrain*

4. My feet are in the stirrups and my rope is on the side,
   Show me a horse that I can't ride. *Refrain*

# My Father's House

*Traditional Song from the Southern United States*
*Arranged by Rosemary Jacques*

1.–3. Won't you come with me to my fa-ther's house, To my fa-ther's

house,        to    my    fa - ther's house?      Won't    you    come    with      me

to    my    fa - ther's house,
1. There   is   peace,        peace,        peace.
2. There   is   joy,          joy,          joy.
3. There   is   love,         love,         love.

**Student Page 27**

## *Lucy Locket*

*Street Rhyme*
*Arranged by G. LeNorth*

*Simply*

Lu - cy Lock - et     lost   her   pock - et,    Kit - ty   Fish - er   found     it.

Not   a   pen - ny    was   there   in   it,    On - ly   rib - bon 'round     it.

# Pizza, Pizza, Daddy-o

*Singing Game from the United States*
*Arranged by Joyce Kalbach*

# Down, Down, Baby

*African American Clapping Song*
*Arranged by Ned Ginsburg*

(Spoken)
Grandma, Grandmama, sick in bed,
Called the doctor and the doctor said,
"Let's get the motion of the head, ding dong,
Let's get the motion of the hands, clap clap,

Let's get the motion of the feet, stomp stomp,
Put it all together and what do you get?
Ding dong, clap clap, stomp stomp.
Say it all backwards and what do you get?
Stomp stomp, clap clap, ding dong!"

# The Music's in Me

*Words and Music by Jill Gallina*

# Miss Mary Mack

*African American Clapping Game Song*
*Arranged by Rosemary Jacques*

1. Miss Ma - ry Mack, Mack, Mack, All dressed in
black, black, black, With sil - ver but-tons, but-tons, but-tons, All down her

1. back      back      back.
2. fence,    fence,    fence.

3. 'ly,      'ly,      'ly.

2. She asked her mother,
    mother, mother,
   For fifteen cents, cents, cents,
   To see the elephants,
    elephants, elephants
   Jump over the fence, fence, fence.

3. They jumped so high,
    high, high,
   They touched the sky, sky, sky,
   And never came down,
    down, down,
   'Til the fourth of July, 'ly, 'ly.

# Frog in the Millpond

*Additional Verses by Bryan Louiselle*

*Traditional from the United States*
*Arranged by Ting Ho*

Frog in the mill-pond, Can't get him out. Take a lit-tle stick And stir him a-bout.

2. Frog in the millpond,
   Hops pretty quick.
   Better use a net;
   He doesn't like the stick.

3. Frog in the millpond,
   Hides in the muck.
   Broke out of the net
   With froggie kind of luck.

# Four in a Boat

*Play-Party Song from Appalachia*
*Arranged by Joyce Kalbach*

1. Four in a boat and the tide rolls high, Four in a boat and the tide rolls high,

Four in a boat and the tide rolls high, Wait-ing for a pret-ty one to come bye and bye.

2. Choose your partner and stay all day,. . .
   We don't care what the old folks say.

3. Eight in a boat and it won't go 'round,. . .
   Swing that pretty one that you just found.

# *Way Down in the Schoolyard*

*Traditional*
*New words and musical arrangement by Sharon, Lois and Bram*
*Arranged by Georgette LeNorth*

# Good Mornin', Blues

*Edited and New Additional Material by Alan Lomax*

*New Words and New Music Arranged by Huddie Ledbetter*
*Piano Arrangement by Joseph Joubert*

# El juego chirimbolo (The Chirimbolo Game)

*English Words by Alice Firgau*

*Singing Game from Ecuador*
*Arranged by Marilyn J. Patterson*

El    jue - go chi - rim - bo - lo,    ¡qué bo - ni - to es!    Con un
This    game is chi - rim - bo - lo;    Play and you'll have fun.    First one

pie,    o - tro pie,    u - na ma-no, o - tra mano,    un co - do,    o - tro co - do.    El
foot,    oth-er foot;    Then one hand,_ oth - er hand;_    One el-bow,    oth-er el-bow.    This

co - do,    El jue - go chi - rim - bo - lo,    ¡qué bo - ni - to es!    ¡Hey!
el - bow.    We're play-ing chi - rim - bo - lo.    Now the game is done.    Hey!

# Clouds of Gray

*Words and Music by Katinka S. Daniel*
*Arranged by Carol Jay*

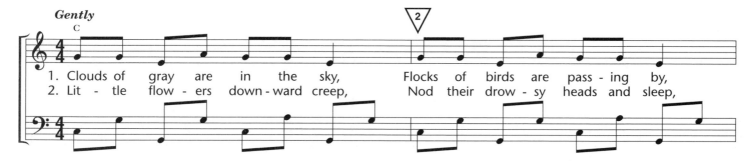

1. Clouds of gray are in the sky,    Flocks of birds are pass - ing by,
2. Lit - tle flow - ers down - ward creep,    Nod their drow - sy heads and sleep,

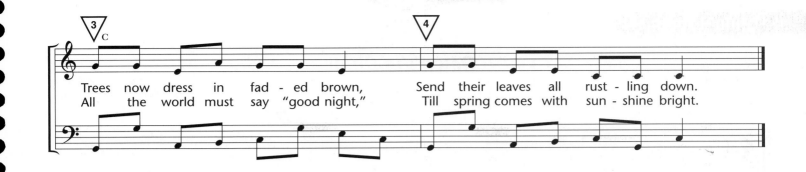

Trees now dress in fad-ed brown, Send their leaves all rust-ling down.
All the world must say "good night," Till spring comes with sun-shine bright.

## I See the Moon

*Melody by Denise Bacon, Adapted*
*Arranged by Georgette LeNorth*

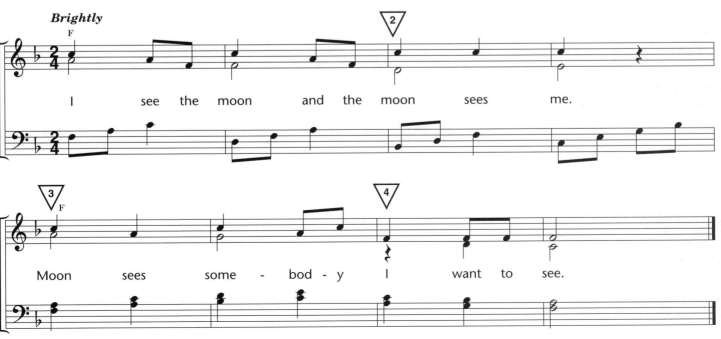

I see the moon and the moon sees me.

Moon sees some-bod-y I want to see.

# Down the Ohio

*River Shanty*
*Arranged by Rosemary Jacques*

# Achshav *(Awake! Awake!)*

*English Words by David Eddleman*

*Folk Song from Israel*
*Arranged by Joyce Kalbach*

# *Ayelivi*

*Story Song from Ghana*
*Arranged by Komla Amoaku*
*Piano Arrangement by Betsy Washington*

**Sadly**

*Solo*
A - ye-li - vi____ no ku - do mi do ba ba____ n'a ye li vi.
A - ye-li - vi____ has lost her way and can't find____ her moth - er dear.

*Chorus*
Yie yie mi do ba ba____ n'a - ye - li - vi.
Wah, wah, we feel sad for____ A - ye - li - vi.

# *Step in Time*

Words and Music by Richard M. and Robert B. Sherman
Arranged by John Girt

1. Kick your knees up, step in time! Kick your knees up,
2. Spin a - bout and step in time! Spin a - bout and

step in time! Nev - er need a rea - son, nev - er need a rhyme,
step in time! Nev - er need a rea - son, nev - er need a rhyme,

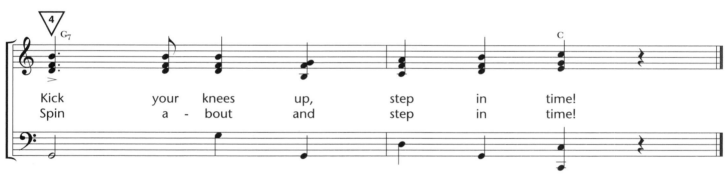

Kick your knees up, step in time!
Spin a - bout and step in time!

3. Link your elbows, step in time! . . .
4. 'Round the circle, step in time! . . .

5. Flap like a birdie, step in time! . . .
6. Step in time, step in time! . . .

# Tideo

*Play-Party Song from Texas*
*Arranged by Georgette LeNorth*

Pass one win-dow Ti-de-o, Pass two win-dows Ti-de-o,
Pass three win-dows Ti-de-o, Jingle at the win-dow Ti-de-o.

Ti-de-o.

Ti-de-o, Ti-de-o, Jin-gle at the win-dow Ti-de-o.

# Amarillo Armadillo

*Words and Music by Robert Demmert*

**With a beat**

Am - a - ril - lo Ar - ma - dil - lo, that's some shell! Still you move a - round quite well.
Am - a - ril - lo Ar - ma - dil - lo, ar - mored back. Grab some grubs and have a snack.

# Crawfish!

Words and Music by Papillion
Arranged by Buddy Skipper

30

step or two.                                                                    Then put your

hands  in the  air, do  like the  craw - fish    do. __

§ 1 REFRAIN                                                                    2
       All                                                                       All
       Solo
       D
                    Craw - fish!   Got  to   do   a  lit - tle  mud  bug    boo-gie, Craw -

Solo
C7
fish!  do the  mud  bug    jit - ter-bug  boo-gie, Craw - fish!
                                                                         All
                                                                         G

(Note: Recording contains Instrumental Verse)

Craw - fish-in' to the left, Craw - fish-in' to the right, Let's all go craw - fish-in' on a Sat - ur - day night, Craw - fish-in' to the front, Craw - fish-in' to the back. Let's all go craw - fish-in' with a craw - fish___ sack! Craw - fish-in' go-in' up, Craw -

## Ein Männlein steht im Walde *(A Little Man in the Woods)*

*German Words by Hoffmann Von Fallersleben*
*English Words by Bryan Louiselle*

*Folk Song from Germany*
*Arranged by Anita P. Davis*

1. Ein Männ-lein steht im Wal - de ganz still und stumm; es hat von lau - ter
1. A lit-tle fel-low stands in the woods a - head, He wears a pur-ple

Pur - pur ein Mänt - lein um. Sagt, wer mag das Männ - lein sein,
coat with a hint of red. Tell me who this man can be,

das da steht im Wald al - lein mit dem pur-pur-ro - ten Män - te - lein?
stand-ing there so pa-tient-ly, Stand-ing all a - lone in the woods a - head?

## Allá en la fuente *(There at the Spring)*

*English Words by Luis Eliezar*

*Folk Song from Mexico*
*Arranged by Rosemary Jacques*

A - llá en la fuen - te ha-biá un cho - rri - to; se ha-ciá gran-do - te, se ha-ciá chi -
A lit - tle spring, feel-ing ver - y fick - le, Be-gan a flood, then be-came a

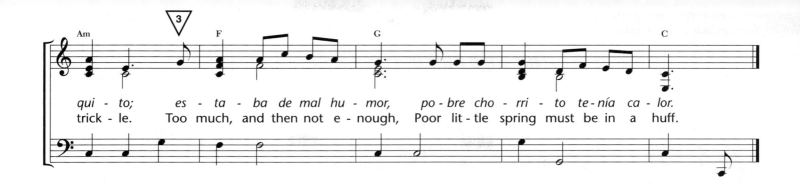

quito;    es - ta - ba de mal hu - mor,    po - bre cho - rri - to te - ní - a ca - lor.
trick - le.    Too much, and then not e - nough,    Poor lit - tle spring must be in a huff.

## I Fed My Horse

*Folk Song from North Carolina*
*Arranged by David Deschamps*

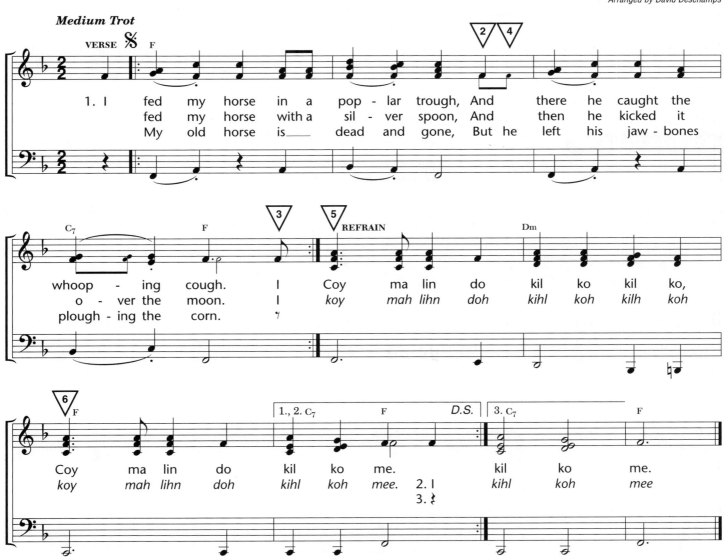

**Medium Trot**

VERSE

1. I    fed    my    horse    in a    pop - lar    trough, And    there    he    caught    the
   fed    my    horse    with a    sil - ver    spoon, And    then    he    kicked    it
My    old    horse    is____    dead    and    gone,    But he    then    left    his    jaw - bones

whoop - ing    cough.    I    Coy    ma    lin    do    kil    ko    kil    ko,
o - ver    the    moon.    I    koy    mah    lihn    doh    kihl    koh    kilh    koh
plough - ing    the    corn.

REFRAIN

Coy    ma    lin    do    kil    ko    me.    kil    ko    me.
koy    mah    lihn    doh    kihl    koh    mee.    2. I    kihl    koh    mee
3.

1., 2.    F    D.S.    3.    F

35

# Naranja dulce (Sweet Orange)

*English Words by Eva Laurinda*

*Latin American Singing Game*
*(Mexico and Costa Rica)*
*Arranged by Anita P. Davis*

1. Na - ran - ja dul - ce, li - món par - ti - do, da - me un a -
1. Sweet hon - ey or - ange, a slice of le - mon, Give me a

bra - zo que yo te pi - do.
hug now, my friend, I'll miss you.

2. Si fueran falsos mis juramentos,
   en otros tiempos se olvidaran.

3. Toca la marcha, mi pecho llora,
   adiós señora, yo ya me voy.

2. It's time to shake hands, true friends are faithful,
   I'll not forget you, I wish you well.

3. The march is playing, it's time to go now,
   Goodbye, my dear friend, I'm sad to leave you.

# Rocky Mountain

*Folk Song from the Southern United States*
*Arranged by Merle Buford*

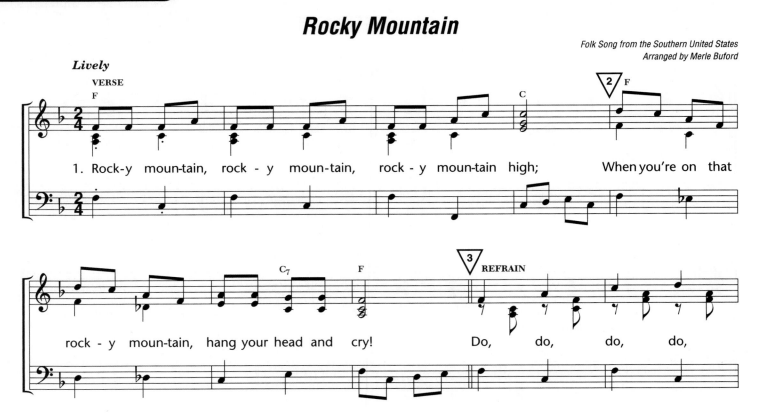

1. Rock-y moun-tain, rock - y moun-tain, rock - y moun-tain high; When you're on that

rock - y moun-tain, hang your head and cry! Do, do, do, do,

**Do re-mem-ber me; Do, do, do, do, Do re-mem-ber me.**

2. Sunny valley, sunny valley,
   sunny valley low;
   When you're in that sunny valley,
   Sing it soft and slow. *Refrain*

3. Stormy ocean, stormy ocean,
   stormy ocean wide;
   When you're on that deep blue sea,
   There's no place you can hide. *Refrain*

**Student Page 100**

## *Sea Shell*

*Words and Music by Pierre Perron*
*Arranged by E. G. McKinley*

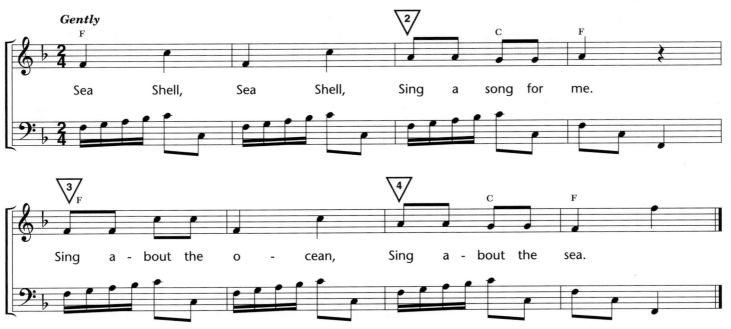

**Sea Shell, Sea Shell, Sing a song for me.**

**Sing a - bout the o - cean, Sing a - bout the sea.**

# Ise oluwa

*Yoruba Folk Song from Nigeria*
*Arranged by Joseph Joubert and James Rooker*

# Waiting for the Traffic Light

*Words and Music by David Connors*
*Arranged by Carol Jay*

**Swing Style**

We're wait-ing for the traf-fic light to turn to green. If it ev-er happens it re-

mains to be seen. As we wait for the light we will start to move.

We can feel the rhy-thm and get in-to the groove. Move to the right.

Move to the left. Move in a way that you like best. Ev-'ry-one back

turn 'round and 'round, Ev-'ry-one for-ward, touch the ground.

# Abiyoyo

Bantu Lullaby
Arranged by John Detroy

# Banana

Words and Music by Flor De Caña
Arranged by David Eddleman

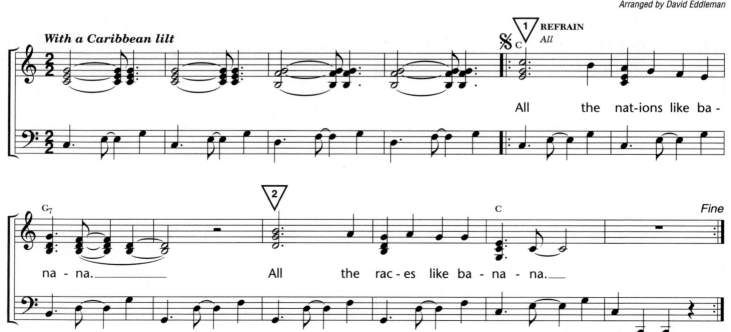

# La tormenta tropical *(The Tropical Storm)*

Words and Music by Juanita Newland Ulloa
Arranged by John Girt

2. *Entonces cierro las ventanas*
   *el viento soplará.*
   *El cielo estara enojado*
   *y pronto llorará.*
   Refrain.

3. *Por fin sale el sol.*
   *El viento se calló.*
   *las gotas se apagan*
   *la lluvia se paró.*
   Refrain.

2. We'll stay inside while it's raining.
   Let's get the windows shut tight.
   The sky is getting dark like it's nighttime!
   Sit here with me 'til it's light.
   *Refrain.*

3. We'll listen to the storm raging.
   Glad we're inside on this day.
   Tomorrow we'll go out and see puddles,
   When the dark clouds all go away.
   *Refrain.*

# Dinah

*Folk Song from the United States*
*Arranged by Beth Davidson*

No one's in the house but Di-nah, Di-nah, No one's in the house but me, I know.

No one's in the house but Di-nah, Di-nah, Strum-min' on the old ban - jo.

# Old Brass Wagon

*Play-Party from the United States*
*Arranged by Ting Ho*

1. Cir - cle to the left, old brass wag-on; Cir-cle to the left, old brass wag-on;
2. Cir - cle to the right, Cir-cle to the right,

Cir - cle to the left, old brass wag - on; You're the one, my dar - lin'.
Cir - cle to the right,

3. Swing, oh, swing,. . .

4. Promenade right,. . .

5. Walk it up and down,. . .

6. Break and swing,. . .

## Frère Jacques *(Are You Sleeping?)*

*Folk Song from France*
*Arranged by Wallace Schmidt*

# A Song That's Just for You

Words and Music by Bryan Louiselle

# How Many Miles to Babylon?

*Game Song from England*
*Arranged by Georgette LeNorth*

# Plant Four Seeds

*Southern Proverb*

*Music by Students from Upper Nyack, NY*
*Arranged by Rosemary Jacques*

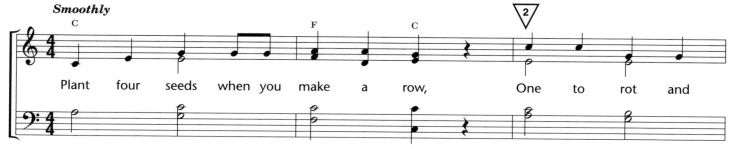

one    to   grow,    One    for  the  pig - eon  and    one    for  the  crow.

## Ha'kyo jong  (School Bell Sounding)

*English Words by David Eddleman*

*School Song from Korea*
*Words and Music by Mary Kimm Joh*
*Arranged by Sammy Lee*

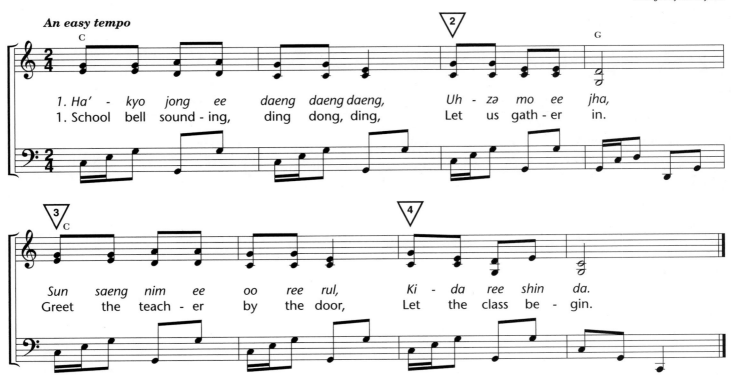

**An easy tempo**

1. Ha' - kyo jong ee    daeng daeng daeng,    *Uh - zə mo ee jha,*
1. School bell sound - ing,    ding dong, ding,    Let us gath - er in.

*Sun   saeng nim ee    oo ree rul,    Ki - da ree shin da.*
Greet  the teach - er    by the door,    Let the class be - gin.

2. *Ha'kyo jong ee*
   *daeng daeng daeng,*
 *Uhzə mo ee jha,*
 *Sa ee joht keh oh nuhldoh,*
 *Khong bu jhal ha jha.*

2. School bell sounding,
   ding, dong, ding,
 Let us gather in.
 Working all together now,
 Learning once again.

**49**

## Adana ya gidelim *(Let's Go to Adana)*

English Words by C.P. Language Institute

*Folk Song from Turkey*
*Arranged by Christopher Hatcher*

## Oh, Watch the Stars

Folk Song from South Carolina
Arranged by Don Kalbach

Oh, watch the stars, see how they run. Oh, watch the stars, see how they

run._____ The_____ stars run down_____ at the

set-ting of the sun. Oh, watch the stars, see how they run.

51

# I See with My Hands

Words and Music by Marcy Marxer
Arranged by Marilyn J. Patterson

*Sincerely*

VERSE

1. I see with my hands The clouds, the sky, the land; The fish that swim in the deep blue sea, The sun that shines on you and me. I see with my hands. REFRAIN See, _____ see, _____ ev-'ry cu-ri-os-i-ty; _____ See, _____ see, _____ in my hands I

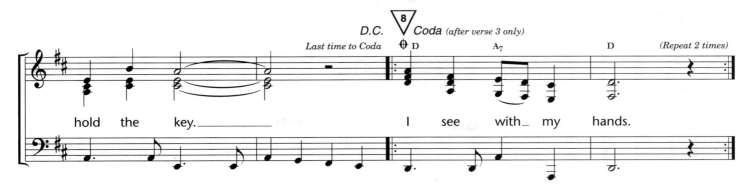

*D.C.* Last time to Coda. Coda *(after verse 3 only)*

hold the key._____ I see with_ my hands.

2. I see with my hands
The clouds, the sky, the land;
A bird, a flow'r, a warm embrace,
And my best friend's smiling face.
I see with my hands. *Refrain*

3. I see with my hands
The clouds, the sky, the land;
A stone, a stream, a melody,
The people in my family.
I see with my hands. *Refrain*

**Student Page 152**

## *Party Tonight!*

*Words and Music by Jill Gallina*

**With a Swing**

All the an-i-mals at the_ zoo_ are hav-ing a par-ty to - night_

Hop-pin' and bop-pin'; roll - in' and rock-in' did you ev - er see such a sight?_

1. Hip - hop - pin' hip - pos the grace - ful danc-ing bears,
2. A rock - in' rhin - o, a waltz - ing pea-cock too,

stomp, stomp-in' el - e - phants___ so loud it hurts our ears.___ A hy-
swing danc-ing, mon - keys and___ a twist-in' Kan - ga - roo.___ There's a

e - na does the hu - la, Oh, what a sight! So
bal - let danc - ing ze - bra,

come on down,___ come on down,___ join our par-ty to - night.___

Student Page 156

## *Mariposita* (Little Butterfly)

English Words by Eva Laurinda

Words and Music by Wilber Alpirez Quesada
Arranged by Marilyn J. Patterson

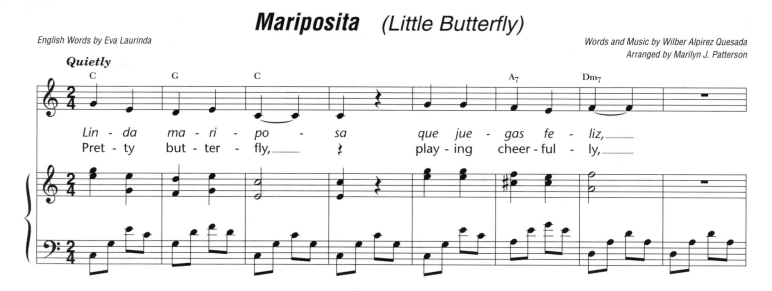

**Quietly**

Lin - da ma - ri - po - sa que jue - gas fe - liz,___
Pret - ty but - ter - fly,___ play - ing cheer - ful - ly,___

## *Hui jia qü* (Home from School)

English Words by David Eddleman

Folk Song from China
Arranged by Kuo Kung

**1** Leisurely

Gong ke__ wan bi__ yao hui jia
When the__ sun is__ sink - ing low,

**2** Shou shi__ shu bao hui jia__ qü **3** Kan jian__ fu mu__ xing ge li
Home - ward__ from my school I__ go, There where__ I know__ I will find

**4** Fu mu__ dui__ wo__ xiao xi xi.
Wait - ing,__ fa - ther and moth - er kind.

56

# Un elefante (An Elephant)

English Words by Alice Firgau

Singing Game from Chile
Words and Music by Claudina de Ferrari
Arranged by Robert Davie

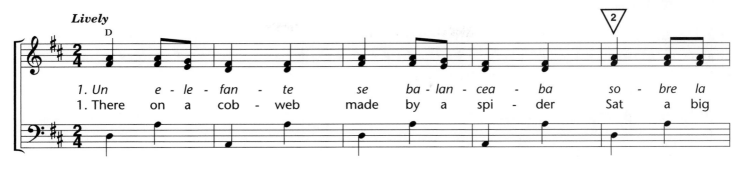

1. Un e - le - fan - te se ba - lan - cea - ba so - bre la
1. There on a cob - web made by a spi - der Sat a big

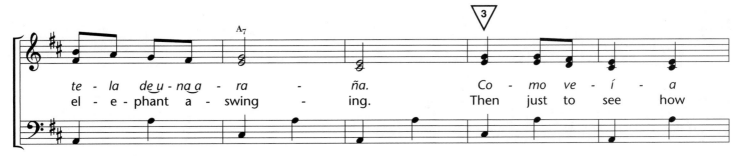

te - la de u - na a - ra - ña. Co - mo ve - í - a
el - e - phant a - swing - ing. Then just to see how

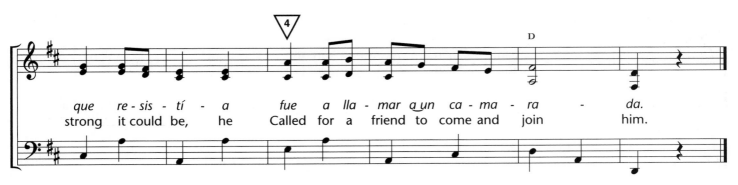

que re - sis - tí - a fue a lla - mar a un ca - ma - ra - da.
strong it could be, he Called for a friend to come and join him.

2. Dos elefantes
se balanceaban
sobre la tela de una araña,
Como veían que resistía
fueron a llamar
a un camarada.

3. Tres elefantes . . .

4. Cuatro elefantes . . .

5. Cinco elefantes . . .

6. Seis elefantes . . .

7. Siete elefantes . . .

8. Ocho elefantes . . .

9. Nueve elefantes . . .

10. Diez elefantes . . .

2. There on a cobweb
made by a spider
Sat two big elephants a-swinging,
Then just to see how strong it could be,
They called for a friend
to come and join them.

3. . . . Sat three big elephants . . .

4. . . . Sat four big elephants . . .

5. . . . Sat five big elephants . . .

6. . . . Sat six big elephants . . .

7. . . . Sat seven big elephants . . .

8. . . . Sat eight big elephants . . .

9. . . . Sat nine big elephants . . .

10. . . . Sat ten big elephants . . .

# Same Train

*English Version by Holsaert-Bailey*

*African American Folk Melody*
*Arranged by Bill Wallace*

**Vigorously**

1. Same train___ a - blow - in' at the sta - tion, Same train,___
2. Same train___ a - com - in' down the line,___ Same train,___

same train.___ Same train___ wait - in' for the peo - ple, Same train,___
Same train___ pick - in' up___ speed,___

same train. ___ Same train___ leav - in' the sta - tion, Same train, ___
Same train___ go - in' like six - ty,

be back to - mor - row, Same train,___ same train.

3. Same train a-chuggin' up the mountain, } 2 times
   Hard pull, hard pull.
   Same train easy down the mountain,
   Same train be back tomorrow, . . .

4. Same train a-passin' all the farmyards, } 2 times
   Same train, same train.
   Same train a-passin' all the farmyards,
   Same train be back tomorrow, . . .

5. Same train a-whistlin' at the crossroads. } 2 times
   Same train, same train.
   Same train a-whistlin' at the crossroads,
   Same train be back tomorrow, . . .

6. Same train a-comin' to the tunnel, . . .
   Same train a-speedin' through the tunnel, . . .
   Same train out in the sunlight,
   Same train be back tomorrow, . . .

7. Same train a-blowin' for the station, . . .
   Same train a-stoppin' at the station, . . .
   Same train a-droppin' all the people,
   Same train be back tomorrow, . . .

# Sing a Rainbow

*Words and Music by Arthur Hamilton*
*Arranged by Bernie Anderson, Jr.*

# The Dinosaur Dance

*Words and Music by Ned Ginsburg*

61

Wag your di-no-saur tail, now hold your di-no-saur stance.

Whad-da-ya know? You're do-in' the di - no-saur dance!

You dance!

Whad-da-ya know? You're do-in the di - no-saur dance!

# All Around the Buttercup

*Traditional Singing Game from the United States*
*Arranged by Martha Hilley*

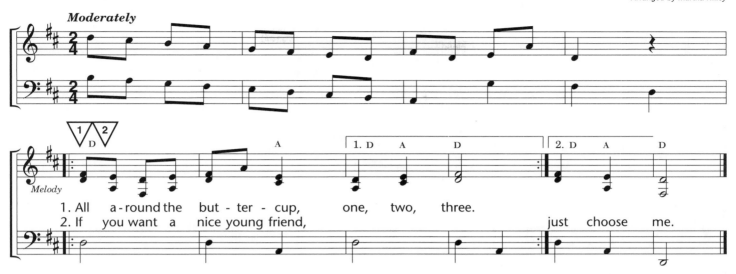

1. All a-round the but-ter-cup, one, two, three.
2. If you want a nice young friend, just choose me.

# Cookie

*Calypso Song from the West Indies*
*Arranged by Leslie Jefferson*

Cook-ie, you sure no-bod-y passed here? No, my friend. friend. Well!

One of me dump-lin's gone! Don't tell___ me so! One of me dump-lin's

gone! Don't tell___ me so! One of me dump-lin's gone! Aw!

# Piñon, pirulín

*English Words by Ellen Traeger*

*Folk Song from Central America*
*Arranged by Donald Scafuri*

2. *Miguel, Miguel, Miguel,*
   *que la vuelta está a la derecha.*
   *Miguel, Miguel, Miguel,*
   *que la vuelta está al revés.*

2. *Miguel, Miguel, Miguel,*
   To the right, to the right, pick a partner.
   *Miguel, Miguel, Miguel,*
   To the left, to the left, pick a friend.

# When the Saints Go Marching In

*African American Spiritual*
*Arranged by Don Kalbach*

1. Oh, when the saints_____ go march-ing in,_____ Oh when the saints go march - ing in,_____ Oh, Lord, I want to be in that num - ber____ When the saints go march - ing in.

2. Oh, when the stars refuse to shine, . . .

3. Oh, when I hear that trumpet sound, . . .

# Cheki, morena *(Shake It!)*

English Words by Alice D. Firgau

Singing Game from Puerto Rico
Arranged by Ting Ho

# The Farmer's Dairy Key

*Folk Song from the United States*
*Arranged by Marilyn J. Patterson*

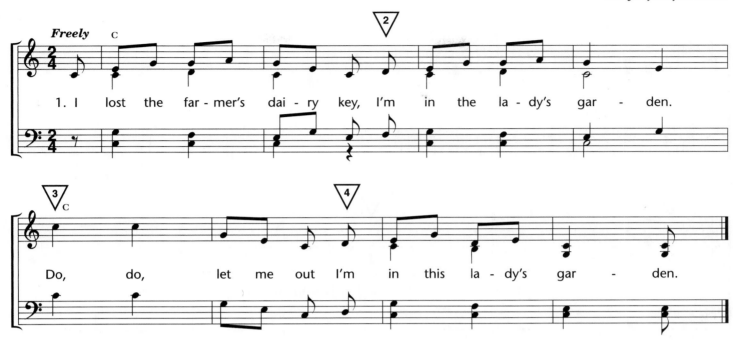

2. A brass key and a silver lock,…

3. A cornstalk fiddle and shoestring bow,…

# Ja-Da

*Words and Music by Bob Carleton*
*Arranged by James Roberts*

It's so sooth-ing and ap - peal-ing to me,___ It goes Ja - Da,

Ja - Da,   Ja - Da,  Ja - Da, Jing, Jing,   Jing.___

# But the Cat Came Back

*Words and Music by Josef Marais*
*Arranged by Elaine Thomas*

2. Freddie put him on a ship and they headed for Ceylon.
   The ship was overloaded more than twenty thousand ton.
   Not far away from shore the cargo ship went down,
   There wasn't any doubt about it, everybody drowned. *Refrain*

3. Then he put the cat aboard with a man in a balloon,
   Who would give the cat away to the man in the moon.
   The balloon didn't rise, it burst in bits instead,
   And ten miles from the spot, they found the man stone dead. *Refrain*

# Caballito blanco   (Little White Pony)

*English Words by Bryan Louiselle*

*Folk Song from Mexico*
*Arranged by Carol Jay*

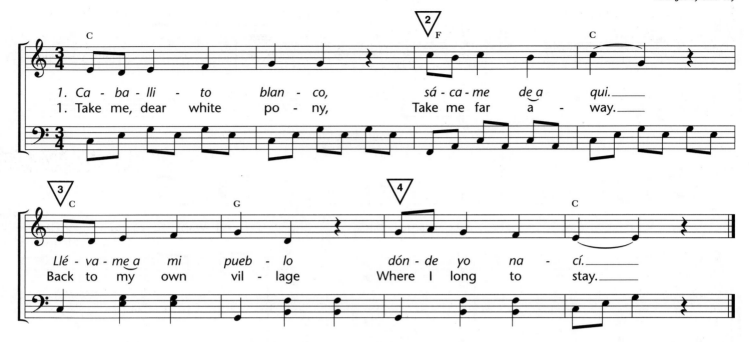

1. Ca - ba - lli - to blan - co, sá - ca - me de a qui.____
1. Take me, dear white po - ny, Take me far a - way.____

Llé - va - me a mi pueb - lo dón - de yo na - cí.____
Back to my own vil - lage Where I long to stay.____

2. *Tengo, tengo, tengo*
   *tu no tienes nada.*
   *Tengo tres borregas*
   *en una manada*

3. *Una me da leche,*
   *otra me da lana,*
   *Y otra mantequilla,*
   *para la semana.*

2. I have quite a fortune,
   You don't have a penny.
   I've three lambs to care for;
   You do not have any.

3. One gives milk each morning,
   One provides her wool
   One whose gift of butter
   Keeps the larder full.

Repeat verse 1          Repeat verse 1

# Boysie

*Lullaby from Trinidad*
*Arranged by Carol Jay*

**Quietly**

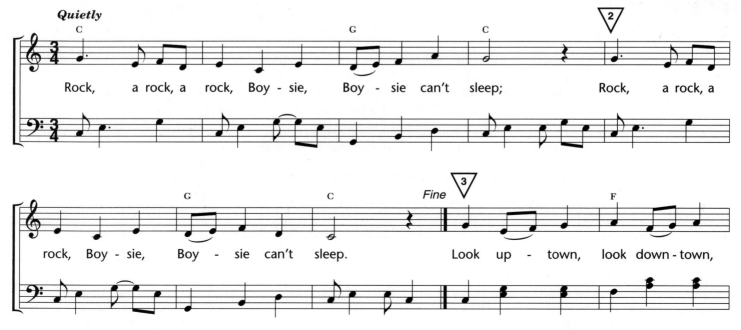

Rock, a rock, a rock, Boy - sie, Boy - sie can't sleep; Rock, a rock, a

rock, Boy - sie, Boy - sie can't sleep. Look up - town, look down - town,

*Fine*

find Boy-sie there: Look up-hill, look down-hill, find Boy-sie there.

## Sleep, Baby, Sleep

*Lullaby*
*Adapted by Cheryl Warren-Mattox*
*Arranged by John Girt*

1. Sleep, sleep, ba-by sleep,_____ Go through dream-land's path.

But I warn_____ you, yes___ I do. That the tor-toise is ver-y

near. Yes, the tor-toise is ver-y near._____

2. Sleep, sleep, baby sleep,
   Do just as I say.
   Go to sleep, sleep baby sleep.
   And the tortoise will go away.
   Yes, the tortoise will go away.

3. Sleep, sleep, baby sleep.
   Dream sweet dreams.
   You are safe, Mommy is here.
   I will always be very near.
   Yes, I'll always be very near.

# Un, deux, trois (One, Two, Three)

Singing Game from France
Arranged by Marilyn J. Patterson

# Shoo, Fly

*Folk Song from the United States*
*Arranged by Cameron McGraw*

Shoo, fly, don't both - er me, Shoo, fly, don't both - er me,

Shoo, fly, don't both - er me, For I be - long to some - bod - y.

I feel, I feel, I feel, I feel like a morn - ing star, I

feel, I feel, I feel, I feel, I feel like a morn - ing star. So,

# Trouble Is a Mountain

*Words and Music by Arthur Cunningham*
*Arranged by Anita P. Davis*

# Great Big House

*Play-Party Song from Louisiana*
*Arranged by Linda Williams*

1. Great big house in New Or - leans, For - ty sto - ries high;
2. Went down to the old mill stream, To fetch a pail of wa - ter;
3. Fare thee well, my dar - ling girl, Fare thee well, my daugh - ter;

Ev - 'ry room that I've been in, Filled with pump - kin pie.
Put one arm a - round my wife, The oth - er 'round my daughter.
Fare thee well, my dar - ling girl, With gold - en slip - pers on her.

# See-Saw Sacradown

*Traditional Rhyme*

*Music by Paul Kapp*
*Arranged by Erma Dowdy*

**Happily**

See - Saw Sac - ra - down, Which is the way to Lon - don town?

One foot up, the oth - er foot down, That is the way to Lon - don town.

# Chicka Hanka

*African American Work Song*
*Arranged by Elaine Thomas*

**78**

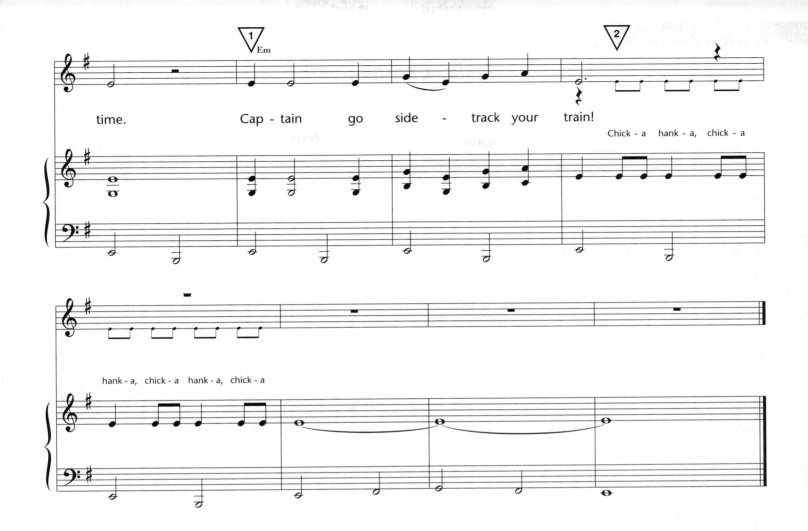

time.        Cap - tain        go        side  -  track your    train!

Chick - a    hank - a,    chick - a

hank - a,   chick - a   hank - a,   chick - a

# Rosie, Darling Rosie

*African American Game Song*
*Arranged by Bill and Pat Medley*

# Kou ri lengay *(The Strength of the Lion)*

Words by Ague Commari

*Game Song from Tanzania*
*Arranged by Edward Corson*

# Ev'ry Kind of Music

Words and Music by David Eddleman
Arranged by Buddy Skipper

# Glad to Have a Friend Like You

Words and Music by Carol Hall
Arranged by Jill Gallina

*Cheerfully*

**VERSE**

1. Jill told Bill that it was lots of fun to cook.

Bill told Jill that she could bait a real fish-hook.

So they made oo-ey goo-ey choc-olate cake stick-y lick-y sug-ar
And they sat by the riv-er and they fished in the wa-ter and they

top and they gob-bled it and gig-gled.
talked as the squirm-y worm-ies wig-gled.

**REFRAIN**

Sing-in' Glad to have a

friend like you, fair, and fun, and skip-pin' free. Glad to have a

friend like you, and glad to just be me.

2. Peg told Greg she liked to make things out of chairs.
   Greg told Peg sometimes he still hugged teddy bears.
   So they sneaked in the living room and piled all the pillows up and
   Made it a rocket ship to fly in.
   And the bears were their girls and boys and they were the astronauts
   Who lived on the moon with one pet lion.
   *Refrain*

# Bob-a-Needle

*African American Ring Game*
*Arranged by Ting Ho*

# *My Foot's in My Stirrup*

*Folk Song from Tennessee*
*Arranged by Carol Jay*

**Soulfully**

1. My foot's in my stir - rup, my reins in my hand, I'm
2. I'm go - ing to Geor - gia, I'm go - ing to Rome, I'm
3. Go build me a cab - in on the moun - tains so high, Where the

goin' a - way to leave you for some far dis - tant land.
go - ing to Geor - gia to make it my_____ home.
wild_____ birds and tur - tle dove can hear my sad_____ cry.

## A-Tisket, A-Tasket

*Folk Song from the United States*
*Arranged by Mark A. Miller*

# *We're All Gonna Shine Tonight*

Camp Song from the United States
Arranged by David Eddleman

# I Got Shoes

African American Spiritual
Arranged by Anita P. Davis

2. I got a song, you got a song,
   All God's children got a song;
   When I get to heaven,
     gonna sing my song;
   I'm gonna sing all over God's heaven, . . .
   Gonna sing all over God's heaven.

3. I got wings, you got wings,
   All God children got wings;
   When I get to heaven
     gonna put on my wings;
   I'm gonna fly all over God's heaven, . . .
   Gonna fly all over God's heaven.

## Shake Them 'Simmons Down

*Play-Party Song from Texas*
*Arranged by Elaine Thomas*

1. Cir-cle right, do-oh, do-oh, Cir-cle right, do-oh, do-oh, Cir-cle right, do-oh, do-oh, Shake them 'sim-mons down.

2. Circle left, . . .
3. Boys to the center, . . .
4. Girls to the center, . . .
5. Promenade all, . . .
6. Swing your corner, . . .

## El florón *(The Flower)*

*English words by Verne Muñoz*

*Singing Game from Puerto Rico*
*Arranged by Carlos Forjador*

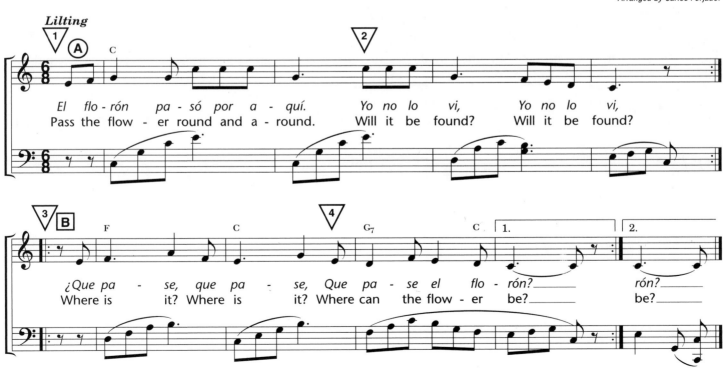

El flo-rón pa-só por a-quí. Yo no lo vi, Yo no lo vi,
Pass the flow-er round and a-round. Will it be found? Will it be found?

¿Que pa-se, que pa-se, Que pa-se el flo-rón?____ rón?____
Where is it? Where is it? Where can the flow-er be?____ be?____

# Ragtime Cowboy Joe

Words by Grant Clarke

Music by Lewis F. Muir and Maurice Abrahams
Arranged by Bernice Anderson, Jr.

# Happy Feet

Words by Jack Yellen

Music by Milton Ager
Arranged by Buddy Skipper

hear a tune, I can't con - trol My danc - ing heels to save my soul.

I keep cheer-ful on an ear-ful of mu - sic sweet,____

"Cause I've got hap - hap - hap-py feet._____

# All the Way Around the World

Words and Music by Katherine Dines
Arranged by Edward Corson

3. This boat's gonna carry love and peace, . . .
*Refrain*

4. This boat's gonna carry hope and strength, . . .
*Refrain*

# El tren (The Train)

*Folk Song from Venezuela*
*Arranged by E. G. McKinley*

# Hello!

Words and Music by Laszlo Slomovits
Arranged by Ting Ho

98

Some-times we shake hands; we wave and we grin.__ We pat each oth-er on the back;_ we say, "Hi! How you

2. In Mexico they say, *"Buenas Días," "Buenas Días."*
In Russia they say, *"Zdrastvooyti," "Zdrastvooyti."*
In Japan, they say, *"Konnichi Wa," "Konnichi Wa."*
In India they say, *"Namaste," "Namaste."*
*REFRAIN*

**Student Page 265**

## *Sawatdee tuh jah* (The Hello Song)

*Folk Song from Thailand*
*Collected by Mary Shamrock*
*Arranged by Ting Ho*

*Sah - wat - dee tuh jah__ rao mahn paup gun,*
When we meet each oth - er, we say hel - lo.

*Tu re chahn__ paup gun sah - wat - dee.*
When we meet,__ we say hel - lo.

# Che che koolay

*Folk Song from Ghana*
*Arranged by Joseph Joubert*

# Zudio

*Traditional Street Song from the United States*
*Arranged by Don Kalbach*

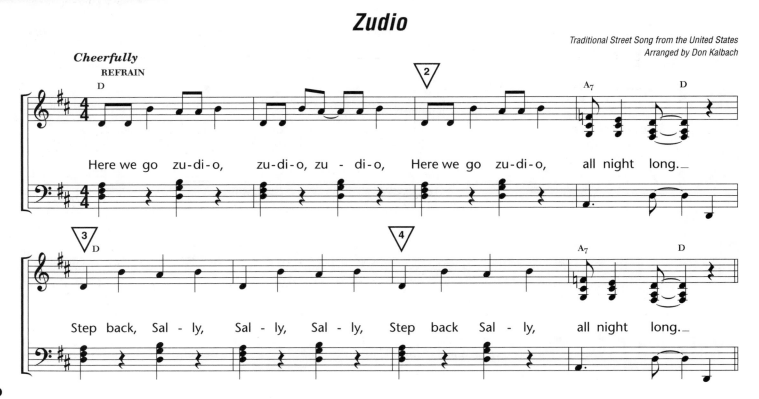

**VERSE**

Walk-in' down the al - ley, what do I see?__ I see a great big man from Ten - nes - see.__

Bet-cha five dol-lars I can catch that man, Bet-cha five dol-lars I can catch that man.__ To the

side, to the side, to the side, side, side;__ To the side, to the side, to the side, side, side,__

side, side, side.__ My ma - ma called the doc - tor, the doc - tor said,__

"Oo, oh,__ I got a pain in my head."__
"Oo, oh,__ I got a pain in my tum."__ To the side, to the side, to the side, side, side;__ To the
"Oo, oh,__ I got a pain in my side."__

side, to the side, to the side, side, side,__ side, side, side.__

## *Kapulu kane* (Puili Game Song)

*Singing Game from Hawaii*
*Arranged by Marilyn J. Patterson*

Ka - pu-lu, pu-lu Ka-ne, Ka - pu-lu, pu-lu Ka-ne, Ka - pu-lu, pu-lu Ka-ne, ku-ka - na - lu - a. Ka-

pu-lu, pu-lu Ka-ne, Ka - pu-lu, pu-lu Ka-ne, Ka - pu-lu, pu-lu Ka-ne, ku-ka - na - lu - a.

## *Ciranda* (A Ring of Roses)

*Singing Game from Brazil*
*Arranged by Vlad Rosco*

Ci - ran - da ci - ran - di - nha, Va - mos to - dos ci - ran - dar. Va - mos
A ring, a ring of ro - ses, Let's all dance a - round to - day. Let's___

dar a me - ia vol - ta, vol - ta e me - ia va - mos dar.
dance 'round in a cir - cle, then go back the oth - er way.

# El tambor (The Drum)

*Folk Song from Mexico*
*Arranged by David Deschamps*

From CHILDREN'S SONGS OF MEXICO, collected and adapted by Roberta McLaughlin and Lucille Wood.

Lyrics (verse 1 / verse 2):

Un tam - bor, me com - pró el do - min - go mi pa - pá, Y a ju - gar me lle - vó por la tar - de mi ma - má. Tra la la la la la la la la la la la la. Tra la la la la la la la la la la la.

Lit - tle drum, lit - tle drum my pa - pa brought me to - day, Lit - tle drum, lit - tle drum my ma - ma taught me to play. Tra la la la la la la la la la la la la. Tra la la la la la la la la la la la.

## Diou shou juan'er  (Hide the Scarf)

English Words by David Eddleman

Singing Game from China
Arranged by Marilyn J. Patterson

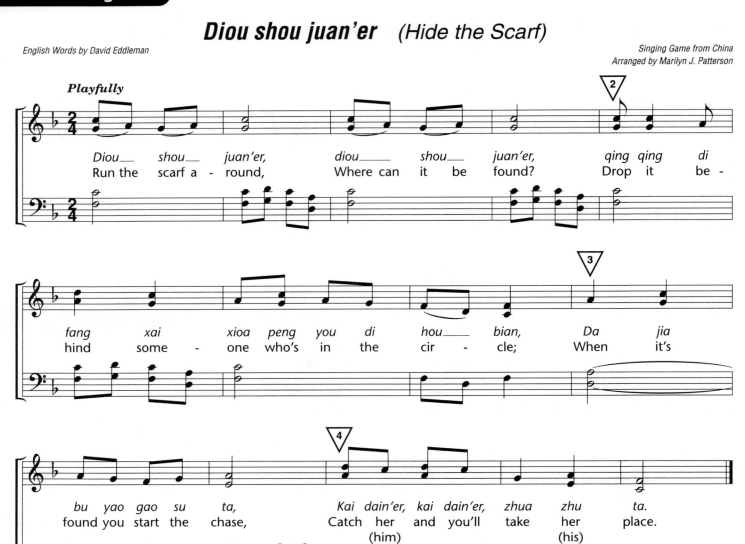

Diou___ shou___ juan'er, diou___ shou___ juan'er, qing qing di
Run the scarf a - round, Where can it be found? Drop it be -

fang xai xioa peng you di hou___ bian, Da jia
hind some - one who's in the cir - cle; When it's

bu yao gao su ta, Kai dain'er, kai dain'er, zhua zhu ta.
found you start the chase, Catch her and you'll take her place.
(him) (his)

## Mon papa  (My Papa)

English Words by Edith Bicknell

Folk Song from France
Arranged by Mary Jean Nelson

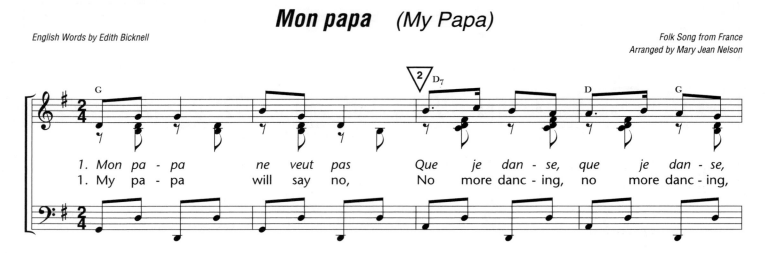

1. Mon pa - pa     ne veut pas     Que je dan - se, que je dan - se,
1. My pa - pa     will say no,     No more danc - ing, no more danc - ing,

Mon pa - pa ne veut pas Que je dan - se la pol - ka!
My pa - pa will say no, No more pol - ka danc - ing now!

2. *Mais malgré sa défense,*
   *Moi je danse, moi je danse,*
   *Mais malgré sa défense,*
   *Moi je danse la polka!*

2. Oh papa, dear papa,
   Let me go and dance the polka,
   Oh papa, dear papa,
   Let me dance the polka now!

**Student Page 283**

## Somebody Waiting

*Play-Party Song from the United States*
*Arranged by Anita P. Davis*

1. As I look in - to your eyes, I be - hold a glad sur - prise, There is some - bod - y wait - ing for me. 2. There is some - bod - y wait - ing, there is some - bod - y wait - ing, There is some - bod - y wait - ing for me.

3. Now choose two, leave the others, . . .

4. Swing the one, leave the other, . . .

# Haere (Farewell)

English Words by David Eddleman

Maori Song from New Zealand
Arranged by Chris Church

# I'm Flying Home

*Words and Music by David Eddleman*

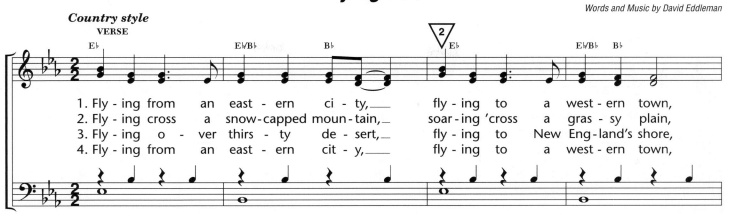

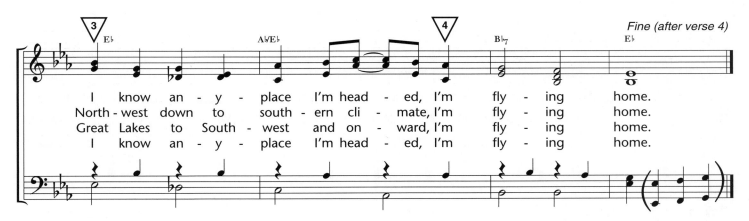

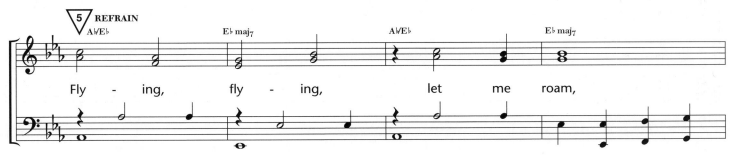

# What Do Animals Need?

*Words and Music by the Banana Slug String Band*
*Arranged by Buddy Skipper*

an - i - mal can live in a rot - ten old log. They live ev - 'ry-where this

whole world round, In the air, land, or wa - ter, and un - der - ground.

Food, wa - ter, shel - ter, that's where it's at, The an - i - mal's home is called it's

hab - i - tat. 2. The blue whale in the o - cean, the tor - toise in the sand, All the

# El coquí  (The Little Frog)

English Words by José-Luis Orozco

Musical arrangement by José-Luis Orozco
Folk Song from Puerto Rico
Piano accompaniment by Marilyn Christensen

# Listen to the Water

Words and Music by Bob Schneider
Arranged by Don Kalbach

wa - ter - side, __ We saw some birds by the wa - ter - side, __
fish
ducks
flowers

Oh, oh, __ by the wa - ter - side, _____ Oh, oh, __ by the wa - ter - side. __

## Chawe chidyo chem'chero *(The Story of the* Kudu*)*

*Shona Ngano Song from Zimbabwe*
*Arranged by Christopher Hatcher*

Cha - we, chi - dyo chem'

che - ro. Cha - we, chi - dyo chem' che - ro.

115

# Der sad to katte *(Two Cats)*

*English Words by Tossi Aaron*

*Folk Song from Denmark*
*Arranged by Per Aarhus*

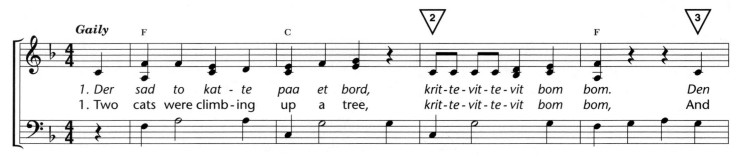

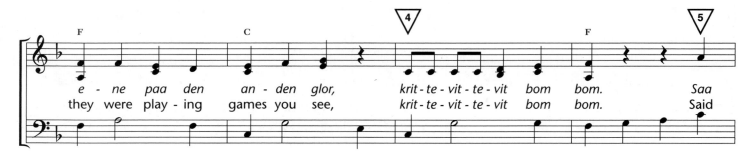

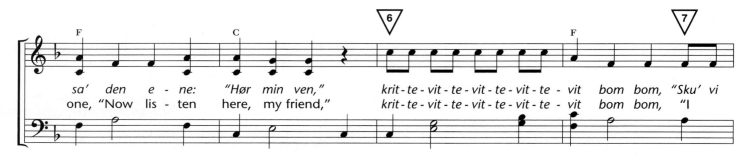

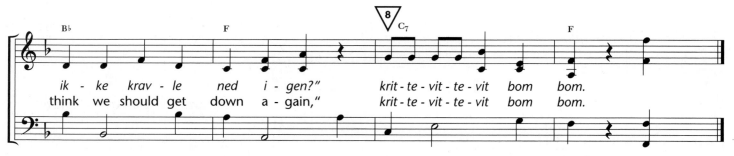

2. *Og da de saa var kommet ned,*
   *krittevittevit bom bom.*
   *Saa sa' den anden: "Hør min ven,"*
   *krittevittevit bom bom.*
   *"Sku' vi ikke dravle op igen?"*
   *krittevittevittevittevit bom bom,*
   *og saa kravlede de op igen,*
   *krittevittevit bom bom.*

2. They scrambled down and took a rest,
   *krittevittevit bom bom.*
   The other said, "No, up is best,"
   *krittevittevit bom bom.*
   So they climbed up that tree again,
   *krittevittevittevittevit bom bom,*
   And that's a game that has no end,
   *krittevittevit bom bom.*

# Leatherwing Bat

*Folk Song from the British Isles*
*Arranged by Bill Wallace*

3. "Hi," said the woodpecker, sitting in the grass,
"Once I courted a bonny lass;
She proved fickle and from me fled,
And ever since my head's been red." *Refrain*

4. "Hi," said the greenfinch as he flew,
"I loved one that proved untrue;
And since she will no more be seen,
Every spring I change to green." *Refrain*

# Rabbit Footprints

Words and Music by David Eddleman

# Deau-deau, ti pitit maman (Sleep, My Little One)

*English Words by Edith Bicknell*

*Lullaby from Haiti
as sung by Germaine Sorel
Arranged by Anita P. Davis*

# I Bought Me a Cat

*Folk Song from Kentucky*
*Arranged by James Rooker*

# Lots of Worms

*Words and Music by Patty Zeitlin*
*Arranged by Edward Corson*

2. I dug the biggest hole I ever did dig,
   The biggest hole. It sure was big!
   And when I got to the bottom, you know what I found
   Way under the ground.

3. I found a worm to go on a fishing pole
   Down in the bottom of that deep, dark hole.
   But I left him alone 'cause he liked his home
   Way under the ground.

4. I found a bumpety bug with big black dots,
   Thirty-three legs and twenty-two spots.
   But I left it alone 'cause it liked its home
   Way under the ground.

5. I found an old sow bug curled up like a ball
   She didn't move from there at all.
   So I left her alone 'cause she liked her home
   Way under the ground
   *Repeat verse 1*

121

# Banjo Sam

*Folk Song from North Carolina*
*Arranged by Bernie Anderson, Jr.*

1. Cat - fish, cat - fish go - in' up stream, Cat - fish cat - fish where you been? I
2. As I was go - in' through the field, A black snake bit me on the heel. I
3. As I was go - in' down the road, I met a ter - ra - pin and a toad. The

grabbed that cat - fish by the snout, I pulled that cat - fish wrong-side out.
grabbed a stick and done my best, And ran my head in a hor - net's nest.
ter - ra - pin, he be - gan to sing. The toad, he cut the pig - eon wing.

Yo ho! Ban - jo Sam!

# Don't Dump Trash

*Words and Music by Jill Jarobe*
*Arranged by Jill Gallina*

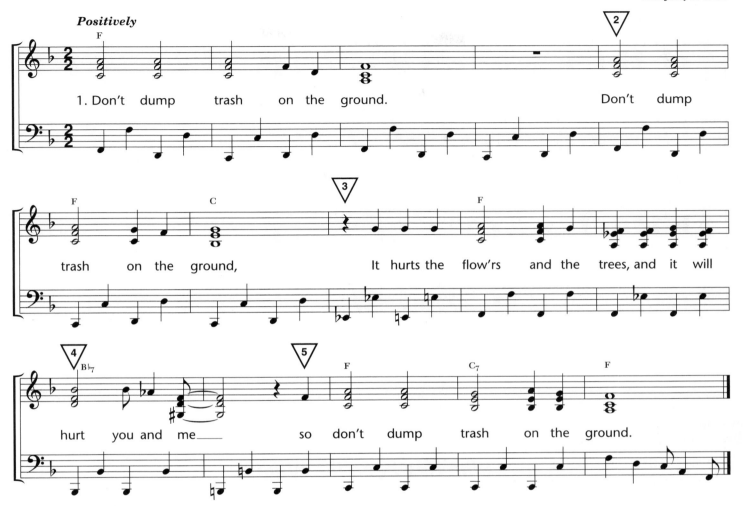

2. Don't dump trash in the sea.
   Don't dump trash in the sea.
   It hurts the fish and the whales
     from their fins down to their tails.
   So don't dump trash in the sea.

3. Don't dump trash in the air
   Don't dump trash in the air.
   All the birds want to fly
     through a pretty clean sky.
   So don't dump trash in the air.

4. Don't dump trash on the moon.
   Don't dump trash on the moon.
   It fills the craters and the cracks
     on the front and on the back.
   So don't dump trash on the moon.

5. Don't dump trash anywhere.
   Don't dump trash anywhere.
   Except in the dump,
     where it's all in a lump.
   No, don't dump trash anywhere.

## Every Morning When I Wake Up

*Words and Music by Avon Gillespie*
*Arranged by Mark A. Miller*

**Student Page 324**

## Who Has Seen the Wind?

*Words by Christina Rossetti*

*Melody from Zion's Harp*
*Arranged by David Eddleman*

through, ... The wind is pass - ing___ through.
by. ... The wind is pass - ing___ by.

## *Let's Go Fly a Kite*

*Words and Music by Richard M. Sherman and Robert B. Sherman*
*Arranged by Robert Davie*

**Smoothly**

Let's go fly a kite Up to the high - est height!

Let's go fly a kite And send it soar - ing

Up through the at - mos - phere, Up where the air is clear.

Oh, lets go___ fly a kite!___

# Falling Rain

Words by Susan Marcus

Music by April Kassirer
Arranged by Mary Jean Nelson

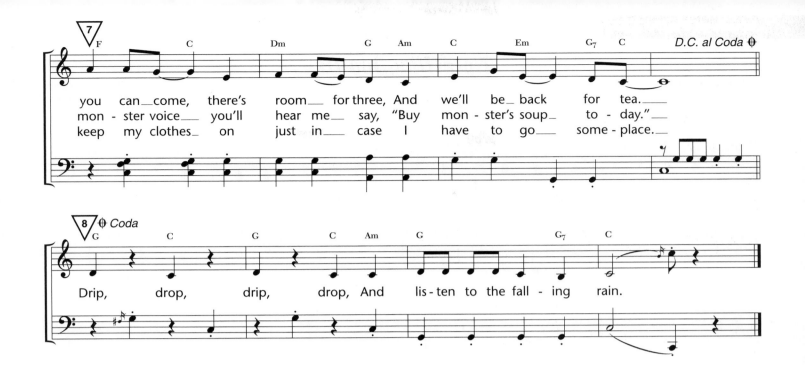

*D.C. al Coda*

you can come, there's room for three, And we'll be back for tea.
mon - ster voice you'll hear me say, "Buy mon - ster's soup to - day."
keep my clothes on just in case I have to go some - place.

**Coda**

Drip, drop, drip, drop, And lis - ten to the fall - ing rain.

# Zip-a-Dee-Doo-Dah

Words by Ray Gilbert

Music by Allie Wrubel
Arranged by Leslie Jefferson

Zip - a-dee-doo - dah, zip - a-dee - ay!

Won - der-ful feel - ing, won - der - ful day.

## *The Rainbow*

Children's Song from the United States
Arranged by Don Kalbach

Smoothly

1. Af - ter the rain is the rain - bow, Af - ter the rain, then the sun comes out a - gain;
2. Red, yel - low, blue is the rain - bow, Or - ange and green and a love - ly vi - o - let;
3. Rain - bows are tell - ing a sto - ry, Rain - bows are say - ing the sun comes out a - gain;

Af - ter the rain is the rain - bow, Pret - ty rain - bow in the sky.
Paint - ing the sky is the rain - bow, Pret - ty rain - bow in the sky.
Af - ter the rain is the rain - bow, Pret - ty rain - bow in the sky.

129

# En nuestra Tierra tan linda

*English Words by Alice Firgau*

*Words and Music by José-Luis Orozco*
*Arranged by Jill Gallina*

2. En nuestra Tierra tan linda
   Pronto va a salir la luna,
   Pronto va a salir la luna
   En nuestra Tierra tan linda.

3. En nuestra Tierra tan linda
   Pronto brillará una estrella,
   Pronto brillará una estrella
   En nuestra Tierra tan linda.

# *Tanabata-sama* (Star Festival)

*Words by Hanayo Gondo with Ryuha Hayashi*
*English Words by Mary Shamrock*

*Music by Kan-ichi Shimofusa*
*School Song from Japan*
*Arranged by Ting Ho*

2. *Goshiki no tanzaku,*
   *Watashi ga kaita,*
   *Ohoshi sama kira kira,*
   *Sora kara miteru.*

2. Choose your fondest wishes to write
   On the strips of paper bright.
   Then tie your wishes high on the tree;
   Stars will grant them, you will see.

# From Sea to Shining Sea

*Words and Music by Gene Grier and Lowell Everson*
*Arranged by Don Kalbach*

from ref - use and_ de - bris.

From sea to shin - ing sea,

# La mar estaba serena (The Sea Is Calm)

English Words by Bob Demmert

Folk Song from Spain
Arranged by David Deschamps

134

## *Sing Me a Story*

*Words and Music by Jill Gallina*

# Puff, the Magic Dragon

*Words and Music by Peter Yarrow and Leonard Lipton*
*Arranged by Cheryl Cronk*

2. Together they would travel
   on a boat with billowed sail;
   Jackie kept a lookout perched
   on Puff's gigantic tail.
   Noble kings and princes
   would bow whene'er they came;
   Pirate ships would low'r their flag
   when Puff roared out his name. Oh!
   *Refrain*

3. A dragon lives forever
   but not so little boys;
   Painted wings and giant rings
   make way for other toys.
   One grey night it happened,
   Jackie Paper came no more,
   and Puff that mighty dragon,
   he ceased his fearless roar.
   *To Verse 4*

4. His head was bent in sorrow;
   green scales fell like rain.
   Puff no longer went to play
   along the cherry lane.
   Without his lifelong friend,
   Puff could not be brave
   so Puff that mighty dragon
   sadly slipped into his cave. Oh!
   *Refrain*

# *Kibungo*

*Story-Song from the Amazon Rainforest*
*Arranged by Ting Ho*

Ki - bun - go o - i bi - cho do ma - to,
Ki - bun - go, oh - oh, beast of the for - est,

Ki - bun - go o - i bi - cho do ma - to.
Ki - bun - go, oh - oh, beast of the for - est.

# *O pião entrou* (The Top Joined the Circle)

English Words by C. P. Language Institute

Game Song from Brazil
Arranged by Jill Gallina

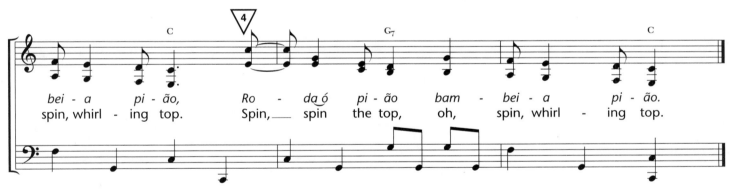

2. *Sapateia no terreiro*
   *ó pião,* (Repeat)
   Refrain

3. *Pega a mão do teo parceiro*
   *ó pião,* (Repeat)
   Refrain

2. Tap away in the clearing,
   dance, spinning top. *(Repeat)*
   *Refrain*

3. Take your partner by the hand,
   spinning top. *(Repeat)*
   *Refrain*

# She'll Be Comin' 'Round the Mountain

*Railroad Song*
*Arranged by Donald Kalbach*

3. Oh, We'll all have chicken and dumplings when she comes. (yum, yum!) . . .

4. Oh, we'll all go out and meet her when she comes, (Hi, there!) . . .

# The Tree in the Wood

*Traditional Cumulative Song from England*
*Arranged by Jill Gallina*

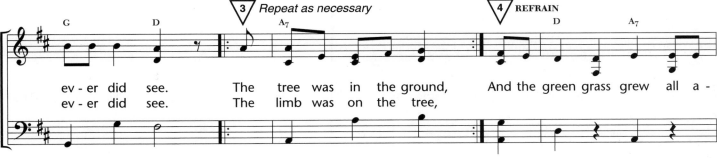

3. Now on this limb there grew a branch
   The finest branch you ever did see.
   The branch was on the limb,
   The limb was on the tree,
   The tree was in the ground,
   *Refrain*

4. Now on this branch there was a bough, . . . *Refrain*

5. Now on this bough there was a twig, . . . *Refrain*

6. And on this twig there was a leaf, . . . *Refrain*

7. And by this leaf there was a nest, . . . *Refrain*

8. And in the nest there was an egg, . . . *Refrain*

9. And in this egg there was a bird, . . . *Refrain*

10. And on this bird there was a wing, . . . *Refrain*

11. And on this wing there was a feather, . . . *Refrain*

12. And on this feather there was a flea, . . . *Refrain*

## The Crocodile

Traditional
Arranged by Don Kalbach

# Deux cocodries *(Two Crocodiles)*

English words by Edith Bicknell

Cajun Singing Game from Louisiana
Arranged by Jill Gallina

# Jig Along Home

Words and Music by Woody Guthrie
Arranged by Rosemary Jacques

jig a - long home. Jig, jig - a jig, jig - a jig a - long home.

3. Mama rat took off her hat,
   Shook the house with the old tom cat.
   The alligator beat his tail on the drum,
   Jig along, jig along, jig along home. *Refrain*

4. The boards did rattle and the house did shake;
   The clouds did laugh and the world did quake.
   New moon rattled some silver spoons,
   Jig along, jig along, jig along home. *Refrain*

5. The nails flew loose and the floors broke down;
   Everybody danced around and around.
   The house came down and the crowd went home,
   Jig along, jig along, jig along home. *Refrain*

# Look Out Below!

Words and Music by Bryan Louiselle

ta - bles can turn in a min-ute     And all of your climb-ing might stop     And

folks you'd as-signed     to     stay     be-hind     Could     sud-den-ly wind

up     on     top.

## It's a Celebration!

Words and Music by Katherine Dines
Arranged by Jill Gallina

# Vamos a la fiesta (Let's Go to the Party)

*Words and Music by Juanita Newland-Ulloa*
*From Canta Conmigo, Vol. 2*
*Arranged by Neil Swanson*

Va - mos a la fies - ta, la  fies - ta, la fies - ta,  Va - mos a la fies - ta  a  go - zar.
Let's go to the par - ty, the  par - ty, the par - ty,  Let's go to the par - ty,  we'll have fun.

To - dos los ni - ñi - tos  muy chi - qui - ti - tos.  To - dos los ni - ñi - tos  a  bai - lar.
All the lit - tle chil - dren,  they'll all be danc - ing.  All the lit - tle chil - dren,  they will sing.

## Skin and Bones

*Folk Song from Kentucky*
*Arranged by Neil Swanson*

1. There  was  an  old  wo - man  all  skin  and bones,  Oo - oo - oo
2. She  lived___ down  by___ the  old  grave yard,

ooh!_____  7. She  open - ed  the  door  and  BOO!

3. One night she thought she'd take a walk, . . .

4. She walked down by the old graveyard, . . .

5. She saw the bones a-lyin' around, . . .

6. She went to the closet to get a broom, . . .

**149**

# The Owl and the Pumpkin

*Words by Betty Barlow and Victoria Shima*

*Music by Betty Barlow*
*Arranged by Martha Hilley*

# *Perot* (Fruit)

English Words by David Eddleman

Traditional Song for Sukkot
Arranged by Neil Swanson

Pe - rot,    pe - rot!    Mi ro - tzeh lik - not    Pe -
Buy fruit!    Buy fruit!    Who will buy my fruit    to

rot le - chag Suk - kot?    A - na - vim ve - ta - pu - chim,    a - na - vim ve - ta - pu - chim,
ce - le - brate Suk - kot?    In the *suk - kah* you will dine,    Grapes and ap - ples, oh, so fine,

Ve - ag - va - ni - yah    lit - lot al gag Suk - kah.
Plump to - ma - toes, too,    are hang - ing there for you.

# Thanksgiving Is Near

*Words and Music by Grace Nash*
*Arranged by Marilyn J. Patterson and Don Kalbach*

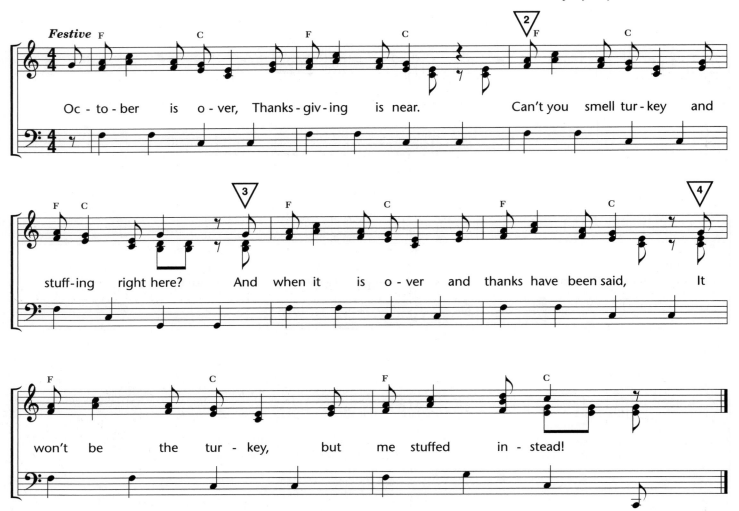

2. The Thanksgiving table is loaded with treats.
   It's hard to use caution and not overeat.
   But when it is over and I'm stuffed in bed,
   I'll wish that the turkey had gobbled instead.

# Chanukah Is Here!

Words and Music by Judith Eisenstein and Frieda Prensky
Arranged by Elaine Thomas

Flick-er lit-tle can - dles; flick-er bright for Cha-nu-kah.

Se - vi-von go spin - ning round and round on Cha-nu-kah. Flick-er lit-tle can - dles,

all eight nights of Cha-nu-kah. Se - vi-von go spin - ning, Cha-nu-kah is here!

# Ner li (The Light)

Words by Levin Kipnis
English Words by David ben Avraham

Music by Mifalei Tarbuth
Arranged by W. R. Colbrook

**Fervently**

Ner_ li__ ner li, ner__ li ta-kik, Ba,_ Cha-nu-kah, ne - ri had - lik,
For_ the_ light, the light_ long a-go, Let_ us_ set the can - dles a - glow;

Ba, Cha-nu-kah, ne - ri a - ir, Ba, Cha-nu-kah, shir - im a - shir.
Come Cha-nu-kah, where light be - longs, Come, Cha-nu-kah, we sing your_ songs.

## O Laufet, ihr Hirten *(Come Running, You Shepherds)*

*English Words By George K. Evans*

*Traditional Silesian Carol from Germany*
*Arranged by Cheryl Terhune Cronk*

# It's Santa—Again!

Words and Music by Elizabeth Gilpatrick
Arranged by Martha Hilley

1. See the rein - deer tak - ing flight_____ On a clear De -
2. Stashed be - hind him, 'way in back_____ I see his e -

cem - ber night._____ Can you see him flash - ing by,
nor - mous pack._____ I have heard it's filled with toys,

Out a - cross the win - ter sky?
For all the girls and all the boys.

You'll miss him if you blink your eye: it's San - ta a - gain!
Hush now, don't you make a noise: it's San - ta a - gain!

# Christmas, Don't Be Late

*Words and Music by Ross Bagdasarian*
*Arranged by David Deschamps*

# Jingle Bells

Words and Music by James Pierpont
Arranged by Wendel S. Evans

Dash - ing through the snow, In a one-horse o - pen sleigh, O'er the fields we

go, Laugh-ing all the way. Bells on Bob-tail ring, Mak-ing spir - its

bright; What fun it is to ride and sing A sleigh-ing song to - night! Oh!

# A Kwanzaa Carol

Words and Music by Reggie Royal
Arranged by Jill Gallina

# Free at Last

African American Spiritual
Arranged by Joseph Joubert

# Valentines

Words and Music by Burt Szabo
Arranged by Anna Leigh

1. Don't you send me hearts and flow-ers if you want to be my val - en - tine,
2. Don't you send me frogs and spi - ders if you want to be my val - en - tine,

Send me frogs and hair - y - leg-ged spi - ders if you want to be my val - en - tine.
Send me hearts and choc-o - late__ flow - ers if you want to be my val - en - tine.

Send me slugs and bugs and toads, cat - er - pil-lars, ants and croc - o - diles,
Send me cards with kitty - cat smiles, but - ter - fly__ wings and cud - dly bears,

Send me snakes and a worm that squirms, and then I'll be your val - en - tine.
Send me straw - ber - ry tarts and cakes, and then I'll be your val - en - tine.

Bugs and but-ter-flies live to - geth - er, snakes and frogs and kit - ty cats, too;

All of us can live to-geth-er; We can all be val - en - tines.

## L'inverno è passato *(Winter Is Over)*

*English Words by Edith Bicknell*

*Folk Song from Switzerland*
*Arranged by Jill Gallina*

L'in - ver - no è pas - sa - to, l'a - pri - le non c'è più, è rit - or - na - to il
The win - ter now is o - ver and Ap - ril rains are gone; It's May a - gain I

mag - gio al can - to del cu - cù. Cu - cù, Cu - cù, l'a -
know for I hear the cuck - oo's song. Cuck - oo, cuck - oo, The

pri - le non c'è più. è rit - or - na - to il mag - gio al can - to del cu - cù.
Ap - ril rains are gone; it's May a - gain I know for I hear the cuck-oo's song.

163

# Haru ga kita  (Springtime Has Come)

*Japanese Words by Takano Tatsuyuki*
*English Words by Patty Zeitlin*

*School Song from Japan*
*Music by Okano Teiichi*
*Arranged by Rosemary Jacques*

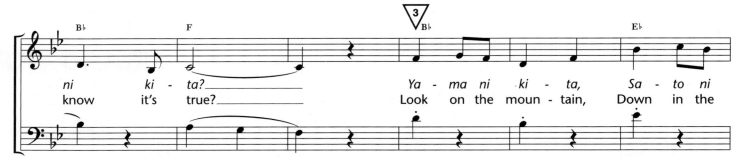

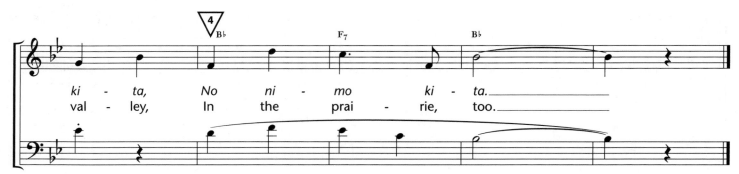

2. *Hana go saku, hana ga saku,*
   *Doko ni saku?*
   *Yama ni saku, Sato ni saku,*
   *No nimo saku.*

3. *Tori ga naku, tori ga naku,*
   *Doko de naku,*
   *Yama de naku, Sato de naku,*
   *No demo naku.*

2. Flowers are blooming, Flowers are blooming,
   Where are they in bloom?
   Up on the mountain, Down in the valley,
   In the prairie, too.

3. Birds are a-singing, Birds are a-singing,
   Where can we hear them sing?
   Up on the mountain, Down in the valley,
   In the prairie, too.

## America, I Hear You Singing

*Words and Music by Barberi Paull*
*Arranged by Elaine C. Thomas*

1. A - mer - i - ca, I hear you sing-ing, A - mer - i - ca, your old sweet song; Our dreams and hopes, it seems, are borne, A - mer - i - ca, in your song.

2. When I sing out your joy - ous an-them, Yes, ev - 'ry time of you I sing, I join your song, A - mer - i - ca, I join in your free - dom song.

# America

Words by Samuel Francis Smith

Traditional

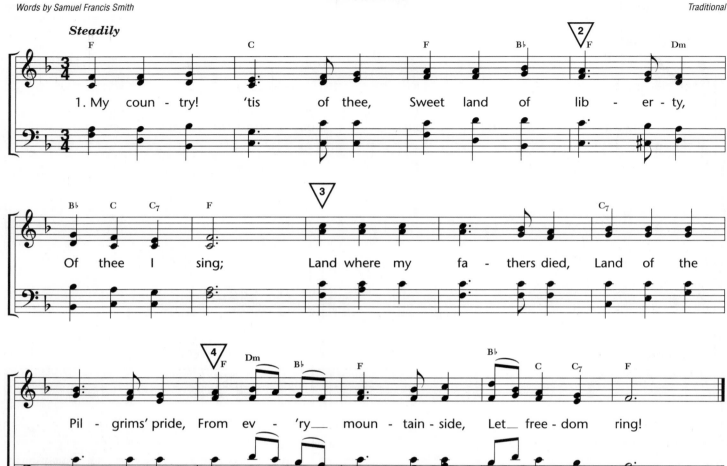

1. My coun - try! 'tis of thee, Sweet land of lib - er - ty,
Of thee I sing; Land where my fa - thers died, Land of the
Pil - grims' pride, From ev - 'ry___ moun - tain - side, Let___ free - dom ring!

2. My native country, thee,
Land of the noble free,
Thy name I love;
I love thy rocks and rills,
Thy woods and templed hills;
My heart with rapture thrills
Like that above.

3. Let music swell the breeze,
And ring from all the trees
Sweet Freedom's song;
Let mortal tongues awake,
Let all that breathe partake,
Let rocks their silence break,
The sound prolong.

# Yankee Doodle

Words by Dr. Richard Schuckburgh

Traditional
Arranged by William Ward

**With spirit**

VERSE

1. ⁊ Fath'r and I went down to camp, A - long with Cap - tain Good - in', And
2. And there was Cap - tain Wash-ing - ton Up - on a slap - ping stal - lion, A -

there we saw the men and boys As thick as hast - y pud - din'.
giv - ing or - ders to his men; I guess there was a mil - lion.

REFRAIN

Yan - kee Doo - dle, keep it up, Yan - kee Doo - dle dan - dy,

Mind the mu - sic and the step And with the girls be hand - y.

167

# CREDITS AND ACKNOWLEDGMENTS

Credit and appreciation are due publishers and copyright owners for use of the following:

4: "Gonna Have a Good Time" Words and music by Bill Shontz, from *Rosenshontz: Share It!* 1992 Rosho Music. Reprinted by permission. 5: "Heigh-Ho" Words by Larry Morey, music by Frank Churchill. © Copyright 1938 by Bourne Co. Copyright Renewed. This arrangement © 2001 by Bourne Co. All Rights Reserved. International Copyright Secured. 6: "Time to Sing" Music by Raffi, words by Raffi, D. Pike, B & B Simpson. © 1985 Homeland Publishing (CAPAC). A division of Troubadour Records Ltd. All rights reserved. Used by permission. 8: "Go Around the Corn, Sally" from *Let's Get the Rhythm of the Band: A Child's Introduction to Music From African-American Culture With History and Song.* Words and music by Cheryl Warren Mattox. Copyright © 1993. Reprinted by permission. 10: "Un pajarito" (A Little Bird) ["El pajaro" (The Bird)], from *A Fiesta of Folk Songs from Spain & Latin America* by Henrietta Yurchenco, copyright © 1967 by Henrietta Yurchenco. Used by permission of G.P. Putnam's Sons, a divison of Penguin Putnam Inc. English version by Pearson Education, Inc. Used by permission of G.P. Putnam's Sons, a divison of Penguin Putnam Inc. 14: "Pizza, Pizza, Daddy-o" from *Circle 'Round the Zero* by Maureen Kenney and MMB Music, Inc. 1974. Reprinted by permission. 15: "Down, Down, Baby" © 1995 Silver Burdett Ginn 16: "The Music's in Me" Words and music by Jill Gallina. Copyright © 1985 by Jenson Publications. This arrangement copyright © 2001 by Jenson Publications. International Copyright Secured. All Rights Reserved. Used by permission. 19: "Frog in the Millpond" (Frog in the Meadow) Additional words © 2002 Pearson Education, Inc. 20: "Way Down in the Schoolyard" from *In the Schoolyard* by Sharon Lois & Bram. Used by permission of Elephant Records. 21: "Good Mornin', Blues" New words and new music arranged by Huddie Ledbetter. Edited and new additional material by Alan Lomax. TRO—© Copyright 1959 (Renewed) Folkways Music Publishers, Inc., New York, NY. Used by Permission. 22: "Clouds of Gray" from *Kodaly in Kindergarten,* (BK-15) words and music by Katinka S. Daniel, Copyright © 1981 Mark Foster Music Co., a division of Shawnee Press, Inc. Delaware Water Gap, PA 18327. International Copyright Secured. All Rights Reserved. Reprinted by permission. 22: "El juego chirimbolo" (The Chirimbolo Game) from *Roots and Branches: A Legacy of Multicultural Music for Children,* by Patricia Shehan Campbell, Ellen McCullough-Brabson, and Judith Cook Tucker. Courtesy World Music Press. English version "The Chirimbolo Game" translated by Pearson Education, Inc. Used by permission of World Music Press. 26: "Ayelivi" arranged by Komla Amoaku from the Ewe speaking people of Ghana. Reprinted by Permission. English version by Pearson Education, Inc. 27: "Step in Time" Words and music by Richard M. Sherman and Robert B. Sherman. © 1963 Wonderland Music Company, Inc. All Rights Reserved. Reprinted by Permission. 29: "Amarillo Armadillo" Words and Music by Robert Demmert. Copyright © 2002 Red Room Studios. 30: "Crawfish!" Words and music by Papillion © 1997, Papillion Inc. publisher. From the album *Cajun for Kids!* Papillion, Music for Little People/Label. Reprinted by permission. 34: "Allá en la fuente" (There at the Spring). *From Arroz Con Leche: Popular songs and Rhymes from Latin America.* Selected and illustrated by Lulu Delacre. Copyright © 1989 by Lulu Delacre. Reprinted by permission of Scholastic, Inc. English version by Pearson Education, Inc. 34: "Ein Männlein steht im Walde" (A Little Man in the Woods), poem by Hoffmann von Fallersleben. Traditional music. Publication: Sing Mit, Unterstufe. Printed by R. Oldenbourg Verlag, München 1975. Used with permission. English version "A Little Man in the Woods" translated by Pearson Education, Inc. Used with permission. 36: "Rocky Mountain" folk song from Southern United States. © 1972 (Renewed) Belwin, Inc. All Rights Reserved. Used by permission. WARNER BROS. PUBLICA-TIONS U.S. INC., Miami, FL 33014. 36: "Naranja dulce" (Sweet Orange) English words © 2002 Pearson Education, Inc. 35: "I Fed My Horse" from *The Kodaly Context* by Lois Choksy. © 1981 by

Prentice-Hall, Inc. Reprinted by permission of Pearson Education, Inc., Upper Saddle River, NJ. 37: "Sea Shell" Words and music by Pierre Perron. Reprinted by permission of Pierre Perron. 38: "Ise Oluwa" a Yoruba Song from Nigeria, arranged by Nitanju Bolande Casel. Copyright © 1989 by Nitanju Bolande Casel, Clear Ice Music. Used by permission. 39: "Waiting for the Traffic Light" © 2002 Pearson Education, Inc. 40: "Banana" from Rainbow Sign. Words and Music by Flor de Caña. Reprinted by Permission. 42: "La tormenta tropical" (The Tropical Storm) © 2000 Juanita Newland-Ulloa, ASCAP. 44: "Dinah" © 1995 Silver Burdett Ginn. 46: "A Song That's Just for You" © 2000 Bryan Louiselle and Frog Prince Music. 48: "Plant Four Seeds" from *Music For Children* Volume 1. American Version by Carl Orff and Gunild Keetman. © 1982 Schott Music Corp. All Rights Reserved. Used by permission of European American Music Distributors LLC, Sole U.S. and Canadian Agent for Schott Music Corp. 49: "Ha'kyo jong" (School Bell Sounding) Words and music by Mary Kimm Joh from *Roots & Branches: A Legacy of Multicultural Music for Children* by Patricia Shehan Campbell, Ellen McCullough-Brabson, and Judith Cook Tucker. Courtesy World Music Press. English version by Pearson Education, Inc. 50: "Adana ya gidelim" (Let's Go to Adana) English words © 2002 Pearson Education, Inc. 51: "Oh, Watch the Stars" from *Folk Songs North America Sings* by Richard Johnston. 1984 by Caveat Music Publishing Ltd., copyright assigned 1988 to G. Ricordi & Co. (Canada) Ltd. Used with permission. 52: "I See With My Hands" Words and music by Marcy Marxer. From *Cathy and Marcy: Nobody Else Like Me.* © 1993 2 Spoons Music (ASCAP). Used with permission. 53: "Party Tonight!" Words and music by Jill Gallina © 2000 Jill Gallina. 54: "Mariposita" (Little Butterfly) English words © 2002 Pearson Education, Inc. 56: "Hui jia qü" (Home from School) Melody copyright © 1946 the Pagoda, World Around Songs, Inc. English version Silver Burdett Ginn. 57: "Un elefante" Words and Music by Claudina de Ferrari, from *Musica Folklorica y Popular Infantil Chilena* by Juan Pérez Ortega. Reprinted by permission. English verson by Pearson Education, Inc. 58: "Same Train" from *Sing a Song* by Charity Bailey © 1955 (renewed) Plymouth Music Co., Inc. Reprinted by permission. 59: "Sing A Rainbow," words and music by Arthur Hamilton. © 1955 (Renewed) Mark VII Ltd. All Rights administered by WB Music Corp. All Rights Reserved. Used by Permission. WARNER BROS. PUBLICATIONS U.S. INC., Miami, FL. 33014. 60: "Dinosaur Dance" Words and music by Ned Ginsburg. © 1991 by Ned Ginsburg. Reprinted by permission. 63: "All Around the Buttercup" from *Let's Sing Together* by Denise Bacon. © Copyright 1971 by Boosey & Hawkes, Inc. Copyright renewed. Reprinted by Permission of Boosey & Hawkes, Inc. 63: "Cookie" from *Leading Young Children to Music*, 6E by Haines and Gerber, © 2000. Reprinted by permission of Prentice-Hall, Inc., Upper Saddle River, NJ. 64: "Piñon, pirulín" from *Fiesta! Mexico and Central America: A Global Awareness Program for Children in Grades 2–5.* Reprinted with permission from © 1993 by Children's Publishing a division of School Specialty, Inc. English version by Pearson Education, Inc. 66: "Cheki Morena" (Shake It!) as remembered by Richardo Morla Rios in *Roots and Branches: A Legacy of Multicultural Music for Children*, by Patricia Shehan Campbell, Ellen McCullough-Brabson, and Judith Cook Tucker. Used by permission. English version by Pearson Education, Inc. 68: "Ja-Da," Words and music by Bob Carleton, with Revised lyrics by Nan Lynn & Ken Lane. 1918, 1939 (Copyrights Renewed) EMI Feist Catalog Inc. All Rights Reserved. Used by Permission. WARNER BROS. PUBLICATIONS U.S. INC., Miami, FL. 33014. 70: "Boysie" from *The Melody Book* by Patricia Hackett. © 1983. Reprinted by permission of Prentice-Hall, Inc., Upper Saddle River, NJ. 70: "But the Cat Came Back" Words and music by Josef Marais. (ASCAP) © 1956, 1984. Used by permission of Marcel Demiranda. 71: "Sleep, Baby, Sleep" from *Shake It To The One That You Love Best* adapted by Cheryl Warren Mattox. Reprinted with permission. 76: "Trouble Is a Mountain" Words and music by Arthur Cunningham. Copyright ©

1979. Used by permission of Mrs. Arthur Cunningham. 77: "See-Saw Sacradown" Music by Paul Kapp from *A Cat Came Fiddling and Other Rhymes of Childhood*, published by Harcourt Brace, 1956. Reprinted by permission by Richard Kapp. 80: "Rosie, Darling Rosie." © Copyright 1974 by Boosey & Hawkes, Inc. Reprinted by permission of Boosey & Hawkes, Inc. 81: "Kou ri lengay" (The Strength of the Lion) by Beatrice Landeck, from *Echoes of Africa in Folk Songs of the Americas*. Used by permission of Olga Rothchild and Edith Langner. 82: "Ev'ry Kind of Music" Words and music by David Eddleman. © 1991 David Eddleman. Used by permission. All Rights Reserved. 84: "Glad to Have a Friend Like You" from *Free to Be...You and Me*. Words and music by Carol Hall. © Copyright 1999 Otay Music, Corp. and Daniel Music (ASCAP). Reprinted by permission. 86: "Bob-a-Needle" © 2002 Pearson Education, Inc. 87: "My Foot's in My Stirrup" from *Sing It Yourself*. Copyright 1978 by Alfred Publishing Co., Inc. All Rights Reserved. Used with Expressed Written Permission of Publisher. 89: "We're All Gonna Shine Tonight" Music and lyrics by Marie Winn and Allan Miller from the *Fireside Book of Fun and Games* published by Simon & Schuster. Music and lyrics copyright © 1966, renewed 1994 by Marie Winn and Allan Miller. Reprinted by permission. 90: "I Got Shoes" © 2002 Pearson Education, Inc. 91: "El florón" (The Flower) English words © 1988 Silver Burdett Ginn. 94: "Happy Feet," Words by Jack Yellen and music by Milton Ager. 1930 (Renewed) Warner Bros. Inc. All Rights Reserved. Used by Permission. WARNER BROS. PUBLICA-TIONS U.S. INC., Miami, FL. 33014. 96: "All the Way Around the World" Words and Music by Katherine Dines. Copyright © Kiddie Korral Music. Reprinted by permission. 97: "El Tren" (The Train) folk song from Venezuela. Canciones de Nuestra Cabaña. Reprinted by permission. 98: "Hello!" Words and music by Laszlo Slomovits. © 1988 ASCAP. Used by permission. 99: "Sawatdee tuh jah" (The Hello Song) © 1998 Silver Burdett Ginn. 100: "Che che koolay" © 1995 Silver Burdett Ginn. 100: "Zudio" Arrangement © 1995 Silver Burdett Ginn. 102: "Kapulu kane" (Puili Game Song) from *Leading Young Children to Music*, 6E by Haines/Gerber © 2000. Reprinted by permission of Prentice-Hall, Inc. Upper Saddle River, NJ. 103: "El Tambor" (The Drum) from *Children's Songs of Mexico*. Copyright 1963 by Highland Music Company. Copyright assigned 1990 Alfred Publishing Co., Inc. All Rights Reserved. Used with Expressed Permission of Publisher. English version by Pearson Education, Inc. 104: "Diou shou juan'er" (Hide the Scarf) a Game Song from China from *Roots and Branches: A Legacy of Multicultural Music for Children* by Patricia Shehan Campbell, Ellen McCullough-Brabson, and Judith Cook Tucker. Courtesy World Music Press. English version by translated by Pearson Education, Inc. Used with permission of World Music Press. 104: "Mon papa" (My Papa) © 2002 Pearson Education, Inc. 105: "Somebody Waiting" © 2002 Pearson Education, Inc. 106: "Haere" (Farewell) traditional Maori Song, edited and arranged by Patricia Shehan Campbell, Sue Williamson, and Pierre Perron. © 1996 Warner Bros. Publications. All Rights Reserved. Used by permission. WARNER BROS. PUBLICATIONS U.S. INC., Miami, FL 33014. English version Pearson Education, Inc. 107: "I'm Flying Home" Words and music by David Eddleman. © 1991 David Eddleman. Used by permission. All Rights Reserved. 108: "What Do Animals Need?" by the Banana Slug String Band. Reprinted by permission. 113: "El coquí" (The Little Frog) from *De Colores and Other Latin Folk Songs for Children* by José-Luis Orozco, copyright © 1994 by José-Luis Orozco. Used by permission of Dutton Children's Books, a division of Penguin Putnam, Inc. and José-Luis Orozco. Recordings for this selection and others by José-Luis Orozco are available from Arcoiris Records, P.O. Box 7482, Berkeley CA 94707. 114: "Listen To The Water" words and music by Bob Schneider. © 1980 Bobally Music. All Rights Reserved. Reprinted by permission. 116: "Der sad to katte" folk song. © Used by permission MMB Music, Inc./Edition Wilhelm Hansen. 118: "Rabbit Footprints" Words and music by David Eddleman. © 1991 David Eddleman. Used by permission. All Rights Reserved. 119: "Deau-deau, ti pitit maman" (Sleep, My Little One) © 2002 Pearson Education, Inc. 119:

"I Bought Me a Cat" © 1968 Silver Burdett Company. 121: "Lots of Worms" Words and music by Patty Zeitlin. Reprinted by permission of Folklore Productions (ASCAP). 123: "Don't Dump Trash" Words and music by Jill Jarboe. Copyright © 1999 Smithsonian Folkways Recordings. SF 45048 Coco Kallis: Environmental Songs for Kids. "Don't Dump Trash" provided courtesy of Smithsonian Folkways Recordings (202) 287-3424. Reprinted by permission. 124: "Every Morning When I Wake Up" words and music by Avon Gillespie. © 1976 Belwin-Mills Publishing Corp. All Rights Reserved. Used by Permission. WARNER BROS. PUBLICATIONS U.S. INC., Miami, FL 33014. 125: "Let's Go Fly a Kite" Words and music by Richard M. Sherman & Robert B. Sherman. © 1963 Wonderland Music Company, Inc. All Rights Reserved. Reprinted by Permission. 126: "Falling Rain" Music by April K. Kassirer, words by Susan Marcus, from the recording *Homefree!* (© SOCAN) Used by permission. 128: "Zip-a-Dee-Doo-Dah" Words and music by Ray Gilbert and Allie Wribel. © 1945 Walt Disney Music Company. All Rights Reserved. Reprinted by Permission. 129: "The Rainbow" by Jean R. Thomas, from *Songs for Very Little Folks*. © 1981 Jean R. Thomas. Used with permission. 130: "En nuestra Tierra tan linda" (On Our Beautiful Planet Earth) from *Diez Deditos* by José-Luis Orozco, copyright © 1997 by José-Luis Orozco, text and musical arrangements. Used by permisson of Dutton Children's Books, a division of Penguin Putnam Inc. and José-Luis Orozco. Recordings for this selection and others by José-Luis Orozco are available from Arcoiris Records, P.O. Box 7482, Berkeley CA 94707. 131: "Tanabata-sama" (Star Festival) Japanese words by Hanayo Gondo and Ryuha Hayashi. Music by Kan-ichi Shimofusa. Copyright © 1960 by Edward B. Marks Music Company. This arrangement copyright © 2001 by Edward B. Marks Music Company. Copyright Renewed. International Copyright Secured. All Rights Reserved. Used by Permission. English version by Pearson Education, Inc. 132: "From Sea to Shining Sea" words and music by Gene Grier and Lowell Everson. © 1991 Heritage Music Press a division of the Lorenz Corporation International copyright secured. All rights reserved. Used by permission. 135: "Sing Me a Story" Words and music by Jill Gallina © 2000 Jill Gallina. 136: "Puff, the Magic Dragon" Words and music by Peter Yarrow and Leonard Lipton. © 1963 Pepamar Music Corp. © Renewed, assigned to Silver Dawn Music and Honalee Melodies. All Rights Reserved. Used by permission. WARNER BROS. PUBLICATIONS U.S. INC., Miami, FL 33014. 138: "Kibungo, Beast of the Forest" from *The Singing Sack: 28 Song-Stories from Around the World*, compiled by Helen East, A & C Black (Publishers) Limited, 1989. Reprinted by permission of the publisher. English version by Pearson Education, Inc. 139: "O pião entrou" from *The Singing Sack: 28 Song-Stories from Around the World*, compiled by Helen East, A & C Black (Publishers) Limited, 1989. Reprinted by permission of the publisher. English version by Pearson Education, Inc. 142: "The Crocodile" © 1995 Silver Burdett Ginn. 143: "Deux cocodries" (Two Crocodiles) used by permission from *Le Hoogie Boogie: Louisiana French Music for Children* by Sharon Arms Doucet. English version by Pearson Education, Inc. 144: "Jig Along Home" Words and music by Woody Guthrie. TRO— © Copyright 1951 (Renewed) 1963 (Renewed) Ludlow Music, Inc., New York NY. Used by Permission. 146: "Look Out Below!" © 2000 Bryan Louiselle and Frog Prince Music. 148: "It's a Celebration!" Words and music by Kathering Dines © 2000 Katherine Dines. 149: "Skin and Bones" collected by Jean Richie. © Jean Ritchie 1952 Geordie Music Publishing Company. Used by permission. 149: "Vamos a la fiesta" (Let's Go to the Party) Words and music by Juanita Newland-Ulloa from *Canta Conmigo (Sing With Me)*, Bilingual Audio and Songbook Series Vol. 1-3 by Juanita Newland-Ulloa, www.juanitamusic.com. Reprinted by permission. 150: "The Owl and the Pumpkin" from *Halloween on Parade* (GF-72). Words by Betty Barlow and Victoria Shima, music by Betty Barlow. Copyright © 1977 Shawnee Press, Inc. Delaware Water Gap, PA 18327. International Copyright Secured. All Rights Reserved. Reprinted by permission. 151: "Perot" (Fruit) a folksong which appeared in *Songs of Childhood* selected and edited by Judith Eisenstein and Frieda

# CREDITS AND ACKNOWLEDGMENTS *continued*

# SONG INDEX

NOTE: These page numbers refer to the actual page in this book. Page numbers for the Pupil Edition appear above the title of each arrangement.